NEW GENERATIONS

40 Years of Birth in Britain

NEW GENERATIONS

40 Years of Birth in Britain

Joanna Moorhead

Published by HMSO in collaboration with
National Childbirth Trust Publishing Ltd.

Production in association with Book Production Consultants plc, 25–27 High Street, Chesterton, Cambridge CB4 1ND, UK.
Design by Georgia King.

Printed and bound by Butler & Tanner Ltd, Frome, Somerset.

Published by HMSO in collaboration with National Childbirth Trust Publishing Ltd, 25–27 High Street, Chesterton, Cambridge CB4 1ND, UK.
© 1996 NCT Publishing Ltd.

A CIP catalogue record for this book is available from the British Library.

ISBN 0 11 702047 8

Picture Acknowledgements

The Publishers would like to thank the following for supplying pictures:

Image Bank: cover (main picture); Hulton Getty Collection: pp12, 13, 15, 16, 18, 19 (bottom), 20 (middle), 28, 30, 31, 32, 33, 35, 50, 51, 55, 56, 80, 91, 93, 101; NCT: pp1, 4, 5, 6, 7, 19 (top), 57; Collections/Anthea Sieveking: p81; MIDIRS: pp96 (bottom), 113; The Advertising Archives: pp21 (bottom), 29, 59, 71; The Vintage Magazine Company: p48; PCD Ltd: p95; HMSO: p94; *Woman* Magazine: p92; Early Learning Centre: p53; Maclaren: p38; Mothercare: pp36, 37, 78, 79, 97; *Daily Express*: p3; *The Times*: p2; *Daily Sketch*: p9; *News Chronicle*: p11; Fisher Price: pp14, 17, 94, 95; *The Oxford Times*: p21 (top); *The Guardian*: p74; D. Tacchi: p10; Fontana: p54; Souvenir Press Ltd: p72; Penguin Books: p68; Britax: p20 (top); Gerald Fox Spalding: p60; Courtesy of Jack Hampshire Pram Museum: p20 (bottom); Camilla Jessel: p77; Ron Sutherland/Science Photo Library: p 96 (top); Mark Clarke/Science Photo Library: p98 (top); Pascale Roche/Petit Format/Science Photo Library: pp98 (bottom), 114.

Every effort has been made to obtain permission for the reproduction of illustrations and photographs in this book. Apologies are offered to anyone whom it has not been possible to contact and omissions will be corrected in future reprints.

Published by HMSO and available from:

HMSO Publications Centre
(Mail, fax and telephone orders only)
PO Box 276, London SW8 5DT
Telephone orders   0171 873 9090
General enquiries   0171 873 0011
(queuing system in operation for both numbers)
Fax orders   0171 873 8200

HMSO Bookshops

49 High Holborn, London WC1V 6HB
(counter service only)
0171 873 0011   Fax 0171 831 1326

68–69 Bull Street, Birmingham B4 6AD
0121 236 9696   Fax 0121 236 9699

33 Wine Street, Bristol BS1 2BQ
0117 926 4306   Fax 0117 929 4515

9–21 Princess Street, Manchester M60 8AS
0161 834 7201   Fax 0161 833 0634

16 Arthur Street, Belfast BT1 4GD
01232 238451   Fax 01232 235401

71 Lothian Road, Edinburgh EH3 9AZ
0131 228 4181   Fax 0131 229 2734

The HMSO Oriel Bookshop
The Friary, Cardiff CF1 4AA
01222 395548   Fax 01222 384347

HMSO's Accredited Agents (see Yellow Pages)
and through good booksellers

Contents

Acknowledgements

With grateful thanks to all those who have generously shared their time and energy to help with the putting together of this book, especially the women who have allowed me to feature their birth stories.

I would also like to thank Patricia Donnithorne and Eileen Abbott in the NCT Library for guiding me patiently through the mass of information there; Mary Newburn and Clodagh Corcoran of NCT HQ; Prunella Briance, Rosaleen Mansfield, Joyce Crosfield, Deirdre Mackay, Gwen Rankin and Eileen Hutton who put me in the picture about the early days of the NCT; childbirth experts Sheila Kitzinger, Janet Balaskas, Sir George Pinker, Professor Lesley Page, Professor James Drife and Caroline Flint, who shared their memories of the way things were and told me about their vision for a better future; TAMBA (Twins and Multiple Births Association) and SANDS (the Stillbirth and Neonatal Death Society) for help in finding some of the women whose stories I have included. My thanks, too, to Linda Price, who has been endlessly flexible in looking after my children as I worked. Finally, special thanks to the people who have been my 'midwife' and 'birth partner' in the bringing to birth of this project: Daphne Metland of NCT Publishing Ltd, and my husband Gary Smith, whose encouragement and support were, as in so many deliveries, absolutely essential.

J. M.

The publishers are indebted to Hulton Getty Collection for their generous help and co-operation with *New Generations*.

Introduction

Some people think childbirth never changes. Women, they reason, have been having babies for millions of years. Since the days of Eve, it's been more or less the same process.

They're wrong, of course. Childbirth has changed – enormously. And over the last 40 years, in Britain especially, it's changed with extraordinary speed. It's changed for midwives. It's changed for obstetricians. It's changed in terms of technology, in terms of mortality rates, in terms of antenatal care. And most crucially of all, though often least acknowledged, it's changed for women. Having a baby in the mid 1990s is a vastly different experience from having a baby in the 1950s. Today's mothers-to-be face incredulity from their own mothers when they describe birthing rooms, pain-relief options, fetal monitors, water tubs, and six-hour hospital stays. 'It wasn't like that in our day,' their mothers cry. 'What happened to enemas/labour wards/10-day stays/nurseries?'

This is the story of what did happen to them. It's the story of what childbirth is like today, and of how things used to be. It isn't a history of obstetrics or midwifery, though of course obstetricians and midwives are crucial players in the tale. It's a history of childbirth as it has affected mothers – and fathers and babies, too.

Weaving a thread through the book are the memories of women who have given birth in different parts of Britain over the last 40 years. Every birth story is unique, but through those collected here I have tried to give a broad spectrum of the types of antenatal care and delivery available in this country over the last four decades.

Relying on memories to write a history can sometimes be difficult, but remembering childbirth is easy for most mothers. Once we have given birth, whatever the experience was like, it stays with us. Some of the women I have spoken to gave birth 35 or 40 years ago, but they can talk about it as though it was yesterday. Not only the details, but the emotions of the day are recalled easily. They have cried, and laughed, and become angry at their memories.

That is why this story matters: because childbirth isn't just something women go through. It's something that changes them as individuals, something that shows them their vulnerability and their strength, something that teaches them about themselves. What happens to a woman during childbirth can be life-shattering, or it can be life-enhancing. It can be a rocky road that leads to doubts and worries, or a strong first step to confident mothering.

It's sometimes said that getting a healthy baby is all that is important, but that's not a theory I'd subscribe to. My first child, Rosie, was born by caesarean section when I was 31 weeks pregnant after I developed severe pre-eclampsia over the space of a weekend. We both recovered physically, after a while, but psychologically I was wrecked for months, and my early relationship with her was deeply affected. My second daughter, Elinor, arrived at 41 weeks after a normal labour and an active delivery. Being in control and achieving the birth I'd wanted has changed my life, made me a more confident and happier mother, and forged my bond with her from the very start.

Childbirth can't always be achieved without obstetric help. Indeed, some women wouldn't want it that way, and for others (including, very probably, both me and my first daughter) it's literally a lifesaver. But it should always be achieved without sacrificing a woman's dignity, choice and right to explanations. At the end of the day, successful childbirth *is* all about a healthy mother and child: but that means a mother and child who are healthy emotionally, as well as physically.

Joanna Moorhead
March 1996

CHAPTER 1

The Birth of Something Better

It began with two births – one an easy delivery for an impoverished young girl in the East End of London some time shortly before the outbreak of the First World War, the other a stillbirth for a middle-class woman four decades later. The two mothers never met, but their lives were connected by a man whose inspiration was to change the face of childbirth in Britain – Grantly Dick-Read, a doctor from Suffolk who became committed to helping women make childbirth an easier and more fulfilling experience.

The birth in the East End was one of the first the young Dr Dick-Read ever attended, but he knew enough to realise it was

Prunella Briance (left), founder of the National Childbirth Trust, pictured with June Monat at the 1957 Festival of Women, held at Wembley.

exceptional. The young woman was offered some kind of pain-killer, but she refused. Afterwards, Dick-Read asked her why. 'It didn't hurt,' she replied. 'It wasn't meant to, was it, doctor?'

That question remained in Dick-Read's mind and became his guiding principle in the years that followed. What heightened the pain of childbirth, he decided, was fear. Fear led to tension, which led to pain. And fear, for the majority of women giving birth in Britain in the

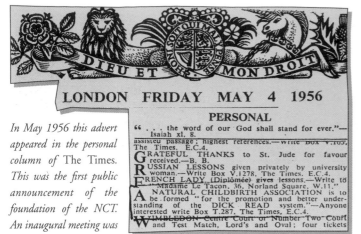

LONDON FRIDAY MAY 4 1956

PERSONAL

" . . . the word of our God shall stand for ever."—
  Isaiah xl. 8.
assisted passage; highest references.—Write Box V.105,
The Times, E.C.4.
GRATEFUL THANKS to St. Jude for favour
  received.—B. B.
RUSSIAN LESSONS given privately by university
  woman.—Write Box V.1278, The Times, E.C.4.
FRENCH LADY, (Diplômée) gives lessons.—Write to
  "Madame Le Tacon, 36, Norland Square, W.11."
A NATURAL CHILDBIRTH ASSOCIATION is to
  be formed "for the promotion and better under-
  standing of the DICK READ system."—Anyone
  interested write Box T.287, The Times, E.C.4.
WIMBLEDON—Centre Court or Number Two Court
  and Test Match, Lord's and Oval; four tickets

In May 1956 this advert appeared in the personal column of The Times. *This was the first public announcement of the foundation of the NCT. An inaugural meeting was held on 29 January 1957 at Caxton Hall in Westminster with Grantly Dick-Read as one of the speakers. The annual subscription was 5 shillings.*

early decades of this century, was based on ignorance. It wasn't so much that they were afraid of what they knew, as of what they didn't know – and couldn't find out.

Dick-Read became a leading proponent of natural childbirth over the following years, so it was to him that a young woman called Prunella Briance turned when she found herself pregnant in the early 1950s. Prunella had already had one child, a son, born by caesarean section in Cyprus. This time around she was determined to have a natural delivery, and she wrote to Dick-Read for information, and read his book *Childbirth Without Fear*.

The book inspired her, but during the delivery disaster struck. The baby was born dead – a consequence, Briance was convinced, of mishandling by medical staff during the labour.

ORIGINAL AIMS OF THE NATURAL CHILDBIRTH ASSOCIATION AS PUBLISHED IN 1956

1. *That women should be humanely treated during pregnancy and in labour, never hurried, bullied or ridiculed.*

2. *That husbands should be present during labour if mutually desired.*

3. *That analgesia should not be forced on women in childbirth (and) nor should labour be induced merely to save time.*

4. *That more emphasis should be given to self-regulated breastfeeding and rooming-in allowed if the mother wants it, and that future maternity units should be designed with this in mind.*

5. *That a mother trained for natural childbirth should be allowed and encouraged to carry out her training fully during labour.*

6. *That all mothers should be encouraged to use natural childbirth for the benefit of themselves and their babies and that posters to this effect should be displayed at all antenatal clinics.*

7. *That the idea fostered by many medical people today that natural childbirth includes routine internal examinations, routine administration of analgesia, routine episiotomy should be dispelled.*

8. *As childbirth is not a disease it should take place in the home wherever possible. If impossible the maternity units should be homely and unfrightening and in no way connected with "hospital".*

Though devastated by her own loss, Briance decided she would devote her time to getting Dick-Read's gospel more widely known, and better understood. She was certain that, had his gentle approach been followed by those who had attended her in labour, her child's death could have been averted. Women and babies, she believed, had suffered enough. Here was a man with ideas for a better way of birth, but his message was not getting through loudly enough. Briance contacted Dick-Read again, and told him of her intention to make his work more widely known.

Briance's first step was to place an advert in the personal columns of *The Times* and the *Daily Telegraph* on 6 May 1956, announcing that 'A natural childbirth association is to be formed for the promotion and better understanding of the Dick-Read system.' The response was overwhelming. Mail, she recalled later, simply poured through the door. 'I was astonished at how many women wanted to get in touch and lend their support. It showed how very great the need was to set up such an association, and it made me all the keener to get it done.'

Some of those who wrote told why they were so resolved to get things changed. 'I am writing to let you know that, even though I objected, they forced a mask over my face as I was in labour,' said one. Another pleaded: 'Couldn't the government *do something* to prevent cruelty in the maternity wards?'

Others, starved of information, wrote enlisting Briance's help. 'Is there a reliable hospital for Dr Dick-Read's work anywhere in the south-east of England?' asked one. 'Where, oh where, can I find a doctor who understands?' begged another.

Most of those who wrote were, like Briance herself, middle-class, establishment women – and there was even a sprinkling of the famous, wealthy and well-connected among their ranks. Several ladies, countesses and viscountesses lent their support, and actresses like Margaret Rawlings and Gina Lollobrigida became involved. It was even rumoured that the Royal ladies were interested in the infant association, and had read Dick-Read's books.

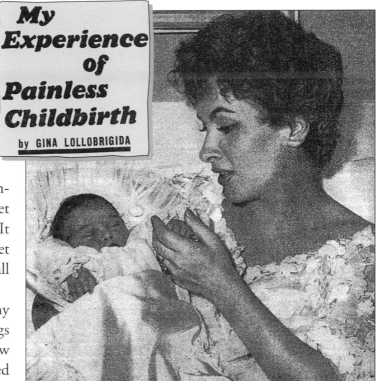

My Experience of Painless Childbirth
by GINA LOLLOBRIGIDA

Right from the beginning of 1957, the pregnancy of film star Gina Lollobrigida was much in the news. In January her choice of a layette for her expected baby was featured in a newspaper article. Her announcement that she and her husband wished their child to be born by natural childbirth methods attracted more attention. On 28 July, media interest was at its peak when she gave birth to a son. As she had hoped, she used no anaesthetics of any kind.

Within weeks the dynamic Briance had organised meetings in supporters' houses in Central London, and plans were in hand for the launch of the organisation. This was held on 29 January 1957 at a packed Caxton Hall, Westminster. It was a huge success, exceeding even Briance's optimistic expectations. The enthusiastic account which went out in the newsletter of the Natural Childbirth

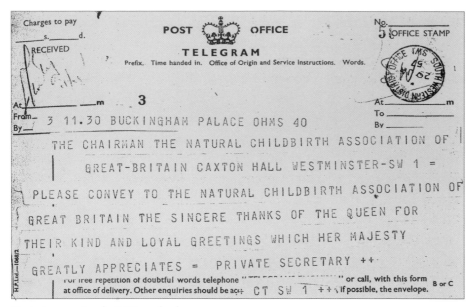

On its inauguration the NCT sent loyal greetings to the Queen and received a reply wishing the new association well.

> 'In the very early days we'd have meetings, about 12 of us, in someone's home in Chelsea. There might have been the odd midwife or physiotherapist among us, but basically we were laypeople. And that was seen as very surprising – in those days, it was doctors and medical people who got involved in childbirth matters, not ordinary mothers. It took a lot of courage to take it on, because we weren't exactly welcomed by some of the medical people. But we supported one another, and we believed very strongly in what we were doing. They were very exciting times – we knew we were making an impact and getting things changed.'
>
> PHILIPPA MICKLETHWAIT,
> NCT PRESIDENT 1971–85

Association of Great Britain, as it was now called, said it all: 'The hall was full. Before it, there was a press conference which was somewhat confused owing to ITV who were busy filming. We are extremely grateful to the Press for all the publicity they have given us – even though in some cases we have had unkind criticism. At least everyone is talking about natural childbirth and its importance to the stability of family life will be realised. We had, in time for the meeting, a telegram from the Queen and letters of congratulation poured in from all over the world where Natural Childbirth Associations or Dick-Read Leagues have already been founded. They, in many instances, are looking to the mother country for a lead and we will do our best …'

The meeting was addressed by the deputy chairman, Betsan Coats, who spoke about her five natural deliveries, and then Dick-Read got to his feet and forecast that happier births could transform the life of Britain in two generations. The rise and fall of great empires, he said, could be linked with a nation's care of its mothers and babies. More speeches followed, and then questions from the floor. Before the meeting was closed, Briance made a pledge: the new organisation, she said, would 'not bludgeon anyone into doing anything but what we will do is to watch, and keep this ideal of childbirth constantly in everyone's minds so that it cannot be forgotten'.

The triumph of the first meeting gave enormous impetus to the infant NCA, and there was a tremendous feeling of excitement and of being in at the start of something significant and far-reaching. The hub of the organisation was very definitely London, but many women from outside the metropolis were interested, and contacted the association. They were invited to become 'area organisers', thus establishing the groundwork for a later string of local groups which would work at childbirth education on a grassroots level. Initially, area organisers were points of contact for others in the area who got in touch. They also held copies of a long-playing record about Dick-Read's theory of natural childbirth, which could be loaned to pregnant women.

In London, meanwhile, the NCA began to screen monthly showings of Dick-Read's film *Childbirth Without Fear* on natural childbirth at a London Review cinema. These attracted a lot of attention, and the cinema was often full. Women who were interested were also encouraged to buy the book, and to team up with other like-minded women in their own areas. But it quickly became clear that listening to a record or watching a film, even in conjunction with reading a book, just wasn't enough. What pregnant women wanted was to join a group at which information about pregnancy and birth would be shared, and support given to help them plan for the kind of delivery they wanted.

Into the breach stepped Jessica Dick-Read, the doctor's wife, who had run classes for pregnant women at her husband's clinic in Johannesburg, South Africa. Here, clearly, was someone with the experience and knowledge necessary to start what would become known as antenatal classes. A few others – Betty Parsons and Sheila Kitzinger among them – were also interested, and so the first antenatal teachers emerged.

The first courses were obviously to some extent trial and error, but from the very earliest days the NCA was firmly committed to being professional, and standards were high. Teachers sat in on other teachers' classes to provide suggestions and constructive criticism, and the views of the mothers-to-be themselves on the way courses should be run were also taken into account (there were no men yet in the antenatal classes – it would be the start of the 1970s before they would be invited in).

The medical profession, though, was sceptical. Although the blossoming NCA listed midwives and physiotherapists among its active ranks, it was still, essentially, an organisation of laypeople. And there was a deep suspicion of laypeople getting involved in what were seen as wholly medical matters – for childbirth, in the 1950s, was considered a completely medical affair. There was no philosophy yet of it as a rite of passage, or a crux point in a couple's relationship, or a time of huge

"In those early days the relationship between us and doctors was a very different one. In common with the social mores of the time, we bowed to the doctors' wishes and were very keen not to do anything to upset them. We would only take women on antenatal courses, for example, if they had their doctor's permission. That attitude altered a great deal during the 1960s, of course, when we were becoming more confident and finding what our role was."

ROSALEEN MANSFIELD, MEMBER OF STREATHAM BRANCH SINCE THE 1950S

Grantly Dick-Read spread his message widely. In February 1958 he was the guest speaker of the Oxford University Medical Society.

OXFORD UNIVERSITY MEDICAL SOCIETY

A lecture
'Some aspects of childbirth without fear'
by
Dr. G. Dick-Read, M.A., M.D.
on Wednesday,
12th February, 1958
at 8.15 p.m.
in the School of Geography, Mansfield Road
A Film will be shown
Non-Members are invited as guests of the President and Committee.

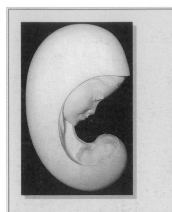

The NCT logo is based on an Innuit carving of a mother and child gleaned from an art shop in Montreal by former NCT president Philippa Micklethwait. Lady Micklethwait was on a visit to Canada and had spent a lot of time looking around maternity hospitals there, when she found herself sightseeing in Montreal where she decided to look for an artefact to take home for NCT headquarters.

The carving seemed perfect and when she returned home another prominent member of the organisation, Amber Lloyd, suggested using it as the basis for the design of the NCT logo, which has simplified over time.

MILESTONES IN THE HISTORY OF THE NATIONAL CHILDBIRTH TRUST

1956: Advert in personal column of The Times *and the* Daily Telegraph

1957: Natural Childbirth Association launched in London

1958: Renamed Natural Childbirth Trust

By *1959:* First antenatal classes taught

1961: Change of name to National Childbirth Trust, and charitable status obtained

1961: The first Education Committee established

By *1962–3:* Constance Benyon FRCS takes over chair of NCT's Executive Committee

1963: First leaflet published – Breathing Control in Labour

By *1966:* Panel of Advisors (medical professionals) in place

1967: Teachers' Panel formed; Breastfeeding Promotion Group formed; Teachers' Broadsheet first published

1969: NCT buys 9 Queensborough Terrace, Bayswater, West London – its first owned property

1971: Philippa Micklethwait becomes NCT President

1975: First NCT research report Some Mothers' Experiences of Induced Labour *published; NCT reports findings and recommendations to an inter-party meeting at the House of Commons; sales company established as a separate company*

1977: Publication by NCT of Expectations of a Pregnant Woman in Relation to her Treatment

1980: Postnatal Support Group, forerunner of Postnatal Committee, formed

1981: Group for Disabled Parents, forerunner of ParentAbility, formed; NCT report Episiotomy – physical and emotional aspects

1985: Eileen Hutton becomes NCT President; Technical Committee becomes Research and Information Group

1987: Organisation moves to Alexandra House, Acton, West London; NCT report Some Women's Experiences of Epidurals *published*

1988: NCT survey Postnatal Infection *published*

1991: NCT gives evidence to the Winterton Committee

1992: Eileen Hutton invited to join the Expert Maternity Group, drawing up the government report Changing Childbirth

1994: Changing Childbirth *becomes government policy*

1995: Barbara Kott becomes President

emotional upheaval. It was a medical condition – an illness, really – and doctors and midwives were the people who could help a woman through it. So who were these NCA women – were they trying to undermine the doctors and interfere, perhaps dangerously, in the care of pregnant women? There was deep suspicion – twice, in its early years, leading members of the organisation were hauled before the British Medical Association to give an account of what they were doing and why.

For its part, the NCA – later the Natural Childbirth Trust, and eventually, in 1961, the National Childbirth Trust – bent over backwards, in those early days, to make its work acceptable to the medical profession. Later, in the second half of the 1960s, its members would accept that the work they were doing was educative rather than medical, and gradually they would gain the confidence to stand up to doctors who sought to interfere in something which was, in fact, complementing rather than clashing with their work. But for the moment they were still finding their feet, and respectability was all. It didn't come easily – from the start, the organisation was labelled cranky and off-beam by some. But gradually, by inviting doctors onto its committees and by insisting that women had their GP's permission before embarking on antenatal courses, several leading medical people were converted to the NCT's cause. Later these triumphs seemed less relevant: but at the time, they ensured the organisation's continued survival.

The 1970s were the battlefield years for the NCT and the medical profession, with the two camps increasingly polarised. During these years childbirth was more medicalised than ever before, and certainly a lot more medicalised than it is now: intervention in the form of (often unnecessary) induction of labour, episiotomies and instrumental deliveries were at all-time highs. The NCT, by now confident of its role, was one of the leading critics of this treatment, and fought – successfully – to change things. Equally important was the alliance forged during these years between the Trust and midwives – to some extent, the NCA realised that buttering up doctors, as it had during its early years, wasn't the key to changing things. But teaming up with midwives – especially the younger and more radical ones now in practice – might be more fruitful. It was to be a successful partnership, and one that is today stronger than ever.

Grantly Dick-Read, whose work inspired the foundation of the NCT.

"*It's difficult for people nowadays to fully appreciate the impact of Dick-Read's writing on mothers who were lucky enough to read his books in the 1950s. To start with, they were written in ordinary English, not medical jargon. In those days, it was unheard of for a doctor to actually want to educate ordinary people about health, but that was what Dick-Read was doing. And his books contained pictures of the baby in the uterus, and diagrams explaining how the cervix dilated. Really, it was revolutionary. You're talking about a decade in which it was considered risqué to use the word "pregnant". Doing what Dick-Read was doing, and then the work done following on from that by the early members of the Natural Childbirth Association, was mould-breaking.*"

"No one told you anything about childbirth in those days, so getting my hands on a copy of Dick-Read's Childbirth Without Fear *was hugely exciting. It was wonderful finding out what was going to happen to my body and my baby during childbirth. There were no antenatal classes so the book was the only kind of preparation around, really. Reading it changed everything for me."*

The 1970s and 1980s saw greater numbers of pregnant women enlisting on antenatal courses, and the Trust's profile continued to grow. By the 1980s it was re-establishing its respectability; not, now, on doctors' terms, but on its own terms. The NCT had become the leading body promoting the rights of women in childbirth, and the leading lay provider of education about childbirth to both parents-to-be and society in general.

The last four decades have seen enormous advances in the treatment of women during pregnancy and childbirth yet now, in the 1990s, the Trust is as busy as ever – busier, in many ways. The issues have changed, but they remain as keen to women today as the original issues were to those 1950s pioneers: antenatal testing, the rising caesarean rate, the provision of facilities for waterbirth, and so on. As a provider of antenatal courses, and as a supporter of breastfeeding mothers, the NCT is the leader in the field – a body respected by health professionals and politicians, and trusted and relied upon by millions of parents throughout Britain.

CHAPTER 2

*1950*s
No Need to Know

'Tasteless,' declared the *Daily Sketch* when, on 4 February 1957, a woman giving birth was shown on television for the first time. In many ways, the verdict summed up the prevailing attitude of the time. Having a baby was something private, animalistic, undignified, and certainly not a subject suitable for general discussion, still less public consumption.

In fact, the television birth was most remarkable for the fact that it was screened at all. It was taken from one of Dr Grantly Dick-Read's films on natural childbirth, and showed fairly graphic scenes of a woman in South Africa holding her baby's hands as it came into the world, and then happily cuddling the child seconds after the delivery. A warning preceded the programme, but the media was still outraged. 'Revolting, beyond the pale,' the *Daily Sketch* continued. 'They showed us a baby being born in all its stark and primitive detail.'

But if the sight was shocking to the viewers at home, it must have shocked in more ways than one. For the birth shown on the BBC that night bore almost no resemblance to the kind of controlled, medicalised experience the vast majority of British mothers would have been put through. Few here would have identified with the South African mother's expression of joy, still less the way in which she seemed to be actively involved in what was going on. A London hospital obstetrician, invited onto *Panorama* to give his critique, found this the most distasteful aspect of all. 'I should not like any patient of mine to be seen groping around to try to bring her own baby into the world,' he spluttered.

The BBC knew its decision to screen the birth would be controversial, but – interestingly – it misjudged the public's response. Teams of telephone operators were standing by for a flood of

> *No one ever asked you about your emotional state when you were pregnant. But then again, back in the 1950s people just didn't talk about their emotions.*

> *Swimming was frowned on while you were pregnant. It was partly that they feared you'd pick up germs at the pool but also, I think, it just wasn't thought proper to display your body in that state.*

The Daily Sketch *in February 1957 reflected the shock and horror expressed by the media the first time a birth was shown on television.*

GRANTLY DICK-READ

GP-obstetrician who pioneered the idea that women needed to be taught about childbirth, and how to relax during it. He believed that if women knew what to expect their fear, and hence pain in labour, would be lessened. His inspiration led to the foundation of the Natural Childbirth Association/Trust, and he became the organisation's first president.

complaints after the programme, but in the event the lines stayed silent. Only two protests were recorded. Could it have been that a population starved of information about this most critical of human experiences was relieved, even grateful, to be allowed at last to witness what was really involved?

Hard facts about childbirth were hard to come by in the 1950s. Men, unless they were medical people, weren't expected to have any interest at all in the entire business. Women, similarly, were judged to have no particular need to know until they had actually embarked upon a pregnancy, by which time the briefest of details could be obtained in a short consultation with the family doctor. But searching, intimate or technical questions were not expected, even from those whose ballooning stomachs showed they were just days from delivery. In 1950s Britain, doctors knew best. They had their ways, they had their reasons, and it wasn't up to the likes of ordinary women to expect too much in the way of explanation or information.

Not, of course, that the doctor necessarily had the information women wanted. In particular, he or she was unlikely to be of much use at the very beginning of pregnancy, when the burning question was: am I actually pregnant? Pregnancy tests, in the shape of the simple, 60-second dipstick affairs we use today, were unknown. You waited until you'd missed two periods, at which stage your doctor could check your uterus and pronounce. Earlier than this, the only way to be sure was bizarre and expensive, and involved injecting morning urine into toads, rats, mice or rabbits, and later examin-

The Newcastle Flying Squad arrives at a row of terraced houses in 1957. From 1935 to 1975 the Newcastle Medical School offered an organised obstetric emergency service. The service, which took the specialist and a nurse to the patient at home and gave treatment for haemorrhage and shock before moving her to a hospital for treatment, was widely copied.

ing them under a microscope for signs of reactions caused by the presence of a pregnancy hormone. In the two-hour rat test, for example, laboratory rats were killed two hours after being injected, and their ovaries checked for signs of congestion caused by the hormone chorionic gonadotrophin. The journalist Myrna Blumberg, who described her pregnancy in a series of articles for the *News Chronicle* in 1957, regaled readers with her experience of a £1 1s 0d "mouse test" at a hospital near her home. On her return visit to hear the verdict, she was told apologetically the test would have to be done again: three of the mice had died inexplicably.

Once pregnancy had been confirmed, one way or another, those who nursed a secret wish to know more about the great adventure ahead would have to find it somewhere other than at the doctor's surgery. The bookshop was the obvious first stop and, though there certainly wasn't a great variety of titles, there were some tomes to which the curious mother-to-be could turn. Most of these majored on the 'safe' subjects of diet, exercise, and the need to get enough rest. Constipation was a major, and recurring, theme, the *Mothercraft Manual* by Mabel Liddiard devoted a whole page to the subject, and an entire chapter to the matter of the layette, but contained virtually nothing about the actual business of labour and birth.

Similarly the *Sunday Express Baby Book* by Mrs Woodman, festooned with pictures of jolly, round-faced babies, had but one solitary paragraph, in a volume of 240 pages, on what one could expect at the delivery itself:

> *'In the delivery room, white with bright lights, you will be taken from the hospital trolley to the delivery table. The nurses will be standing by with the doctor and with their gentle help and encouragement, aided by the science they have studied so long, your baby will be born.'*

So much for answering your questions. On other issues, though, Mrs Woodman was expansive: pages were devoted to foods to be eaten and those to be avoided, curiously, the outlawed list included sausages, duck and pickles. A regular bowel habit was, of course, paramount: 'If you have not already done so, you should form the habit of going to the toilet every morning after breakfast and staying there for some time'.

Indeed, the intricacies of daily life for the pregnant woman were of great concern to Mrs Woodman, who took it upon herself to prescribe what she considered an ideal daily routine:

> *'Rise, brush your teeth, care for your breasts, take a short walk if possible.*
> *Eat breakfast, go to the toilet. Relax, take your time.*
> *Do your housework, keeping windows open and going out of doors for as much of it as possible.*
> *Eat lunch.*
> *Rest for two hours. Wear loose clothes and lie in a quiet room. Sleep if possible, and try to arrange so there will be no interruptions.*

INVESTIGATION BY THE BMA

'Early on the BMA were alerted to look closely at the activities of the National Childbirth Trust, in response to complaints from GPs (un-named to us) about the information being given to patients by local NCT teachers. Philippa Micklethwait, Erna Wright and myself were the representatives who went in response to the Ethical Committee's invitation, and we answered questions from a team of about five senior doctors about who taught classes, what the aim of these were, what was the basis of our knowledge, and who were our advisers. We were told quite gently that they saw no reason to interfere, but advised us to proceed quietly and steadily, rather than make a huge noise about our aims!'

GWEN RANKIN

It's natural birth for MY baby

Myrna Blumberg began a series of articles about her own pregnancy in the News Chronicle on 3 January 1957. At the time, there were no pregnancy tests on the NHS. When she tried to inform herself about natural childbirth, her local library helpfully offered to order books for her – to arrive within six to eight months …

'My second was born at home – a small rented flat – with a midwife on her first solo delivery. After arriving at 8.30pm, (my husband wanted his tea before going to phone her), this midwife did wonders; she unhooked the cord from around the baby's neck and delivered a blue little scrap of a girl at midnight. She then left us all comfortable and tucked up by 2am. At 8am the doorbell rang and my husband sleepily staggered downstairs to let in the GP, supervisory midwife and my wonderful one. "Nurse is worried about the baby," they said, so up they trooped to the flat to find a rosy, round-faced little girl who had suckled at 4am and gone back to sleep.'

CLEONE WRIGHT

❝*Keeping your breasts and nipples clean during pregnancy was considered essential. It was known as 'breast care'.* ❞

Princess Grace of Monaco broke with tradition by continuing to appear in public when her pregnancies were well advanced, and was reported to have used 'natural methods' for the birth of Prince Albert. Prince Rainier holds Princess Caroline.

Spend the rest of the afternoon out of doors if you can. Visit friends, or if it is nice weather, sit in the garden or on the porch, sewing or reading. (A foot-powered sewing machine should not be used in later months of pregnancy; an electric machine is all right.) Prepare and eat dinner. If tired, rest before washing the dishes. Spend the evening reading, sewing at times or with friends, but retire by 10.30pm or not later than 11pm.'

A nice life if you could get it, perhaps, but what about the thousands of pregnant women who already had one, two or more children to look after? Mabel Liddiard was more realistic, at least:

'If possible a rest with the feet up should be taken in the afternoon: an hour is the ideal, but half that time is better than nothing … It should be a complete rest and relaxation with a book, not sitting on a sofa sewing. Where there are small children and no extra help, this is sometimes impossible. In that case the mother must get to bed early or get a real rest in the evening: this the father should insist upon.'

'Duty', a central concept still in these early post-war years, was a running theme through the baby books. Pregnancy wasn't something to be enjoyed or revelled in, it was something to 'do properly', something to get right – for the sake of your baby, of course, but also for the sake of your husband and even your country. Britain needed babies, and looking after yourself so you could provide the nation with a healthy specimen was part of your role as a responsible citizen. So too was 'keeping your pecker up', being 'brave', and not seeming to flinch in the face of the pain ahead. Mrs Hamer of Gosport, in a letter to the problem page of *Mother and Baby* magazine in May, 1956, summed up both this, and the unapproachability of many midwives and doctors:

'My first baby is due in about six weeks' time and I am beginning to get nervous about the birth pains. I have arranged to have a midwife but I am wondering if, should I find the pains too much and want an anaesthetic, the midwife will be able to give me one. I don't like to ask her and so confess my cowardice. Can you help me?'

Eating the 'right' foods was another crucial part of behaving 'properly' in pregnancy; during the early

1950s, when food was still widely rationed, pregnant women were given extra coupons for orange juice and meat. Milk was a crucial ingredient of the mother-to-be's diet: in her book *The Care of the Expectant Mother*, Josephine Barnes recommended two pints a day, as well as one or two eggs or egg yolks daily and calf's liver once a week. Tobacco and alcohol were considered of dubious value, but permissible. Many women lost the taste for cigarettes but, for those who did not, 'a limited amount … may be permitted,' declared Miss Barnes. She was not keen on her patients drinking cocktails, though she allowed them wine, beer or cider with their meals.

Not that much socialising, certainly for middle-class women, would have been expected in pregnancy. It was thought rather distasteful for a woman whose bump was showing to be seen in public, and certainly books on antenatal care did not contain photographs of women in this condition – though attitudes did start to change when celebrities like Princess Grace of Monaco were seen out and about well into her first pregnancy, leading Christian Dior to include maternity dresses in his *haute couture* collection for the first time in 1956. But for the ordinary mortal, being pregnant was something you got on with quietly, behind closed doors. Mrs Woodman, in the *Sunday Express Baby Book*, tactfully suggested that if you did a job where 'your appearance is important', it would probably be wise to stop at around the fifth month. Not that you were to imagine your appearance didn't matter thereafter, though. Dr Winifred de Kok, in *Your Baby – And You*, warned readers:

> 'Don't get the idea that any old thing will do to wear during pregnancy and that a coat will cover up a multitude of sins. You owe it to yourself and your husband to look your very best while you are carrying your baby.'

Antenatal care in the 1950s was either via visits to the family doctor, or at an antenatal clinic staffed by midwives and doctors. Sometimes clinics ran 'mothercraft classes', a new idea to help introduce pregnant women to the idea of impending parenthood. But there was little in the way of discussion about the physical aspects of

DR JOHN BOWLDRY
The doctor whose study of the mental health of homeless children led to a bestselling paperback which implanted the concept of maternal deprivation firmly into the nation's mind. His work centred on the harm that could be done to a child in the longer term by mistreatment during the early years.

Expectant mothers wait their turn at an antenatal clinic in the early 1950s. Advice about coping with the new baby is on display, but little or no information was available about the birth itself.

❝ *My doctor was always telling me not to be afraid of childbirth – but that was all he told me. What I wanted was to know all about it.* ❞

"I hadn't thought about breastfeeding before the delivery, and no one had really mentioned it. When it came to it I didn't find it easy, and there was no help or advice on offer. In the end the midwife said I would go on finding it difficult, so I was given tablets to dry up the milk."

These are the 'absolute essentials' listed by Mrs Woodman in the Sunday Express Baby Book.

THE 1950s LAYETTE

4 sleeveless or long-sleeved vests – cotton, silk or wool, depending on the season and the warmth of your home

4 day gowns of woollen or cotton material

4 short or long nightgowns (fine woollen material for winter, cotton crêpe for summer)

4 dozen napkins 20 or 21 x 40 ins or 20 ins square

4 matinée coats (woollen)

3 blankets or flannel squares 36 x 36 ins

2 carrying shawls

1 cloak, bonnet, gloves

1 hood

Leggings, Overalls, Booties, Safety pins

pregnancy or childbirth at these, still less any talk of emotions or feelings. In general, they were rather busy places, with women sitting round in circles on hard chairs knitting and sewing. Making baby vests, and learning to knit tiny jackets, were considered vital skills. Some of the more avant-garde of the classes included antenatal exercises which were usually practised fully-dressed under the direction of a physiotherapist, in military drill-like fashion.

Only a tiny minority of women had the chance to sample the radically different approach to antenatal training which was, by the late 1950s, being pioneered by the first teachers of the newly-formed Natural Childbirth Association. Betty Parsons, whose classes were held in London, was among them – she taught groups of 12 women at a time, and encouraged them to speak freely and frankly about their worries and about what was actually going to happen to them during labour and birth. Including husbands, though, was not on the agenda – and before admitting any pregnant woman to her class, Mrs Parsons always checked with the woman's doctor to get his or her 'permission' for the patient to attend.

The crux of the Parsons philosophy was to banish fear from the mother-to-be's mind by boosting her confidence, so she embarked on labour believing in her ability to cope. She believed that learning to relax was the key, and emphasised how important it was to learn and practise this skill. But equally crucial was what she called learning to live in the moment. 'One must accept what is now,' she would say. 'That is a rule of life, and it is also a rule of labour.'

This fostering of informed confidence within a woman was an idea decades ahead of its time – for most 1950s mothers-to-be, information came as grim and gory whispered memories from friends or sisters who had already given birth, and usually included little to inspire confidence. This was

still the era of antenatal knowledge via old wives' tales, and for many old wives the main object seemed to be trumping the horror of the previous story. Childbirth, you were told in hushed tones, was unbearably painful. What 'they did to you' was often too terrible to relate, but you'd never forget it afterwards. Nothing was spelled out precisely, few women would have named their body parts, or explained exactly what they meant. And it was in this atmosphere of innuendo, of half-stories, of heavy hints, that many women learnt to fear childbirth. Many medical people were well aware of it: one Harley Street obstetrician used to say he wished his mothers-to-be could be kept away from friends who'd already had babies. But only a few recognised what now seems so plain: that the only way to banish fear was to give women the straight facts.

Given that women in the 1950s knew very little, and thought they had much to fear, it is unsurprising that the general trend was away from home birth – which by 1955 accounted for exactly a third of all deliveries – and towards giving birth in a medical institution. This did not necessarily mean a hospital; maternity homes, most of which had been established between the wars, were still very popular. In these and, to a lesser extent, on the hospital labour wards, midwives ruled the roost.

And the midwives, suggested Donald Buckley in *The Way to Easy Childbirth*, were often preferred by labouring women, who believed they would be more likely to have their views heard:

> 'You may even find that there is a tendency for your doctor to disbelieve you, when you say that you have no pain and do not want any pain-reliever … A high percentage of women do not wish for any anaesthetic at all, but their wishes are not always respected when they should be. Have it out with your doctor and nurse beforehand and see that they understand that if you signify "No" to any attempt to "relieve" you, that you mean "No" and they are not to force it on you. There is no doubt it is often used when it is not necessary.'

Dr Dick-Read quotes the case of a matron of a large country maternity hospital who was puzzled as to why so many women asked to be looked after by the nurses and

> 'In the early 1950s food rationing still applied, but pregnant women got extra coupons for meat, cheese and butter, and there was an allowance for extra fresh milk too. Orange juice could be collected from the local authority clinic as well – it was the concentrated type. No exercise classes were on offer, and no one ever went through the actual birth process with you. Old wives' tales abounded, and if you were either nervous or had a vivid imagination it could all get out of hand very quickly.'
>
> MARGARET THOMAS
> ON GIVING BIRTH IN 1954

Baby bath demonstrations using a doll established the right way to do things and the sense that only the experts knew how to handle a baby.

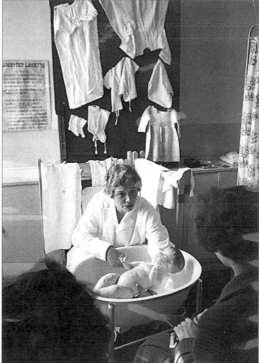

not by the medical men who attended the hospital. Finally, she enquired the reason and was told, 'Because the doctors all make us have chloroform whether we want it or not, and the nurses don't.'

What were the options for pain relief for the 1950s mother-to-be, assuming she was given any options at all? In a column entitled *Pain and Childbirth* in February 1957, *The Sunday Times* doctor listed them thus:

'She can be put to sleep with anaesthetics, or big doses of drugs so that she is more or less unconscious throughout the whole labour.
She can be left to bear the pain until it becomes too unpleasant, and then be given small or medium doses of drugs, such as chloral, pethidine and morphia so that she can rest and sleep between her pains and even have several hours of uninterrupted sleep.
She can be given trilene or gas and air from a machine to inhale. These dull the sensations of pain.
She can receive a course of hypnotism during the pregnancy which, if it is effective, will make the labour virtually painless.

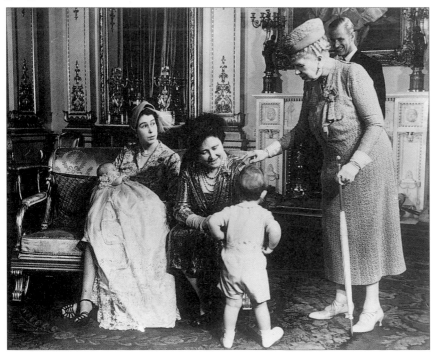

Babies and baptisms were fashionable. Princess Anne, now the Princess Royal, was born in 1950, and photographed in grand style with her mother, grandmother and great-grandmother.

She can receive the full Grantly Dick-Read treatment which, in a large majority of patients is highly successful and is claimed to make the labour not only painless but, in part, positively enjoyable.'

Although the infamous heavy sedation technique known as 'Twilight Sleep', which dated back to the early years of the century, had been more popular as a form of pain relief in the United States, *The Sunday Times* doctor confirmed it was still sometimes used in Britain. He did, however, add a note of caution: 'There are … very real risks for the baby, since it is quite often difficult to rouse it sufficiently to take its first vital breath of air deeply, and to give a good cry at birth.'

For many women who gave birth in a hospital or maternity home in the 1950s, labour meant long, cheerless hours spent alone in a ward reminiscent of Victorian times, with just the grunts and groans of unseen neighbours for company. The concept of a labour partner was unknown: the hours of contractions were to be whiled and wished away on your back, in a hard bed, with a nurse or midwife popping in every so often to do yet another internal examination to find out how far the cervix was dilated. This was usually measured by the size of a coin, so the midwife would say something like 'You're up to half a crown now!' before disappearing off again.

And what, meanwhile, would the hapless father-to-be get up to? Mrs Woodman, in the *Sunday Express Baby Book*, ventured the scenario:

> *'After your arrival at the hospital, he may be told that it will be many hours before delivery. Your doctor or nurse may advise him to go back to the office or home and keep in touch with the hospital. If his remaining at the hospital will make you and him feel better, he may stay in the waiting room and await events. The plight of fathers-to-be has long been the subject of jokes and quips, but it is no fun sitting and worrying, feeling so helpless. Husbands will find the hospital staff helpful and good natured about their many questions … '*

It wasn't until the mother felt ready to push that she would be taken, at last, to the rather daunting delivery room. Dr de Kok warned her readers: 'Do not be alarmed at the appearance of the labour ward, which will look rather like an operating theatre, with cases of instruments and so on. These do not mean a thing … ' But they were guaranteed to put the fear of God into you, just the same. For most women, though, Dr de Kok was right: instrumental deliveries were not common in the 1950s – in 1958, they accounted for only 4.4% of births. Caesarean sections were even more uncommon, at just over 2%.

Pushing was on the back or left lateral, and doctors and midwives expected

"When I started in obstetrics, at the end of the 1940s, the labour ward and delivery rooms were archaic. The instruments were still boiled in a fish kettle, and the approach to patients was, frankly, dictatorial. Husbands weren't allowed in, and visitors were deterred. The delivery of a baby was carried out almost mechanically, and pain-relief was minimal. But as a young doctor I heard a lecture by Dr Grantly Dick-Read, and it was one of the best I ever attended. His gentle, caring attitude to birth was inspirational, and many of us felt he had a great deal to say – though I have to admit that there were still many doubts, at that time, within the profession."

SIR GEORGE PINKER

TOP 20 Names of the 1950s	
BOYS	**G**IRLS
David	Susan
John	Linda
Peter	Christine
Michael	Margaret
Alan	Carol
Robert	Jennifer
Stephen	Janet
Paul	Patricia
Brian	Barbara
Graham	Ann

SOURCE: *THE GUINNESS BOOK OF NAMES,* 7TH EDITION

TOP: *A new father takes a look at his child as the family leaves hospital. Visiting was very restricted and hospital stays long, so this may well be the closest he has been to the baby so far.*

BOTTOM: *The fear of infection was endemic on maternity wards in the 1950s, so much so that mothers had to wear masks while breastfeeding.*

women to lie down, even if they were allowed to sit up in the first stage. The baby emerged into the black-gloved arms of the midwife or doctor, and its first glimpse was of people draped in theatre gowns, their faces hidden by masks. She or he was then turned upside down and suspended briefly by the ankles, to drain any fluid from the mouth and airway and to produce that all-important first cry, considered the hallmark of a successful delivery. The mother, who was probably by now craning to get a glimpse of her new offspring, was usually rewarded after all her hard work by no more than a brief peep before the newborn was whisked off to its cot in the nursery.

And there the baby remained for the next ten days to two weeks, emerging only for four-hourly feeding sessions. Some mothers didn't see their babies for the first 12 or 14 hours if they had an evening delivery; they would be kept in the nursery overnight to allow the new mother her rest, and then wheeled out with the other infants at the morning feed time. The concept of time spent just getting to know one another was totally alien; 1950s babies were there to be controlled and regulated, and it was a task that started at birth. No one considered events from the baby's point of view, and any mother who got a bit weepy about being separated from her child would have been told it was all down to hormones.

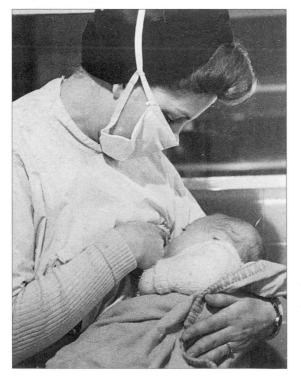

Life on the postnatal ward was never dull, as Mrs Margaret Oliver described in *Mother and Baby* in December 1956.

'A maternity ward is more like a railway station than anywhere else I know – with babies and thermometers and bedpans substituted for trains and arrivals and departures at regular intervals … The days are calm but busy, with feeding times every 4 hours, exercises to do, pills to take, letters to write, meals to eat and visitors to see. The visiting hour is naturally the highlight of the day, and in the previous half-hour there is a frenzy of make-up, titivating and putting on of the best bed-jacket. Supper speedily disposed of, the footsteps of eight breathless husbands are heard in the corridor and for this brief encounter, until the relentless bell sounds, the outside world meets the inside one.'

Remaining in bed for some days after the delivery, and staying in hospital for up to a fortnight, was considered essential. Across the Atlantic, women were already being advised to be up and about straightaway; interestingly, in her *Primer for Pregnancy*, American writer Eve Stanton Featheringill says this was because the experience of new mothers in London during the Blitz had proved it was possible to get up straight after delivery and rush into the shelters with no after-effects. Yet maternity homes here remained unconvinced, partly because they feared the possibility of infection passed on from mother to child, and thought they could more easily contain this risk by keeping the mother bedbound and subjecting her to almost constant bed-baths and washes: morning and night, before and after every feed, and so on.

Hygiene, and an overzealous, almost obsessive approach to preventing infection, also made it difficult for fathers to get any access to their babies. In most hospitals and maternity homes, babies were not wheeled out for visiting-hour – if he wanted a peep at his newborn, the proud dad had to ask permission to go and look through the nursery window at the relevant cot. Some fathers didn't even get the chance of a cuddle until the baby was discharged – small wonder that they didn't expect to be exactly hands-on with babycare once they got home.

But if the new dad was being primed for a spectator's role, and the baby was being trained as a four-hourly feeder who didn't make too many other demands, how was the mother being schooled in her first fortnight as a parent? In the postnatal ward she was waited on, advised to think of herself as rather weak and delicate, and given little in the way of practice in caring for her newborn. Unsurprisingly, this was scant preparation for what awaited her once she got home, and many women found the transition to home life a difficult one. After the *Cranbrook Report* in 1956 recommended providing enough hospital beds to allow for 70% of all births, one of the arguments often put forward for home deliveries was that it made it easier for the mother to adjust slowly to her new role.

And adjusting slowly was easy at home, because, in many areas of the country, local authorities still provided an excellent domiciliary home-help service.

TOP: In a world in which the role of mothers and fathers was strictly divided, few men helped care for the baby. A walk with the baby in the pram may have been one of the few points of contact for this dad and baby.

BOTTOM: The need for fresh air was one of the guiding principles of 1950s chidcare, and even newborns would be put outside in their prams each day in warmer weather.

Typically this meant that for a fortnight after a home delivery a family would have subsidised full-time help with all the household duties and care of any other children.

In other ways, too, home delivery was less daunting than being in a maternity home or hospital; although the midwife who attended you would not necessarily be more forward-thinking than her hospital counterpart, you did have the advantage of getting her undivided attention, and of building up a personal rapport. But the preparations for a home delivery certainly weren't for the faint-hearted. In the April 1956 issue of *Mother and Baby*, Cicely Wrightson described them thus:

TOP: In the early 1900s a folding pram was designed in the United States. This similar pram produced by Marmet was the first to be produced by a British manufacturer. It gradually evolved into the pushchair and the baby buggy of today, which are light, affordable and, above all, portable.

BOTTOM: Feed time was part of the complex routine of hospital life. Rigid schedules of four hourly feeds made no allowance for mothers or babies preferences. Routines were especially important in homes for unmarried mothers such as this one.

'*In the seventh month, all other arrangements having been made, the pregnant mother should prepare the things that will be needed for her home confinement and also prepare the room which is to be used. This should be thoroughly "spring cleaned" and all unnecessary articles and furniture removed in readiness. The essentials are a bed, propped up by strong blocks of wood under each foot to raise the bed to about 2 ft 6 ins off the floor; a table; dressing-table or chest of drawers; two small chairs and the baby's basket or cot. On the table, covered with a towel, piece of clean linen, or clean paper, near the time of the beginning of labour or even before, have ready a "confinement box" containing a fresh, unopened packet of cotton wool; a ditto packet of gauze tissue; some large safety pins; a bottle of antiseptic solution; Vaseline, scissors, olive oil; tape or linen thread for the cord; castor oil; talcum powder; a new nail brush; pure Castile soap; one or two small towels; two teaspoons and two glasses.*'

The pram, regarded as essential by all but the poorest families, was a major item of expenditure, and in many extended families it was passed around for use by the latest baby. The versions that were seen in the 1950s developed from the reversible single-handed prams first produced 60 years before, and black was the standard colour.

Being at home didn't mean your husband (as your partner generally was in those days) would be present for the birth – this was still extremely rare. But he might at least get more scope to see his child in the early days, though some midwives could be very possessive of their newborn charges!

By the end of the 1950s, a small band of women were beginning to insist on a different kind of birth. They called it natural childbirth, and most of them were members of the NCT's precursor, the Natural Childbirth Association. It would be many, many years before the rights they were fighting for would be available to all, but some who were lucky and determined enough were beginning to experience deliveries they could actually feel involved in. Myrna Blumberg, the journalist who wrote about her pregnancy in the *News Chronicle* in 1957, was one of them. Her daughter, Ruth, arrived in a nursing home in what her mother described to readers as 'a jubilant family festival', with her husband present throughout the labour, a doctor who had explained exactly what would happen and sought her views on what she wanted, and a midwife who handed the baby straight to her mother. But for most women, jubilation was not the first emotion after a baby's delivery, and feeling as in control as Ms Blumberg clearly was would, in the decades ahead, become even more of a rarity.

SHEILA KITZINGER

An NCT antenatal teacher who pioneered the idea that women were the active participants, rather than the passive patients, in childbirth. She shifted the focus to birth as an experience, and potentially a major life-enhancing one, for women. Now internationally-recognised for her work as a childbirth educator. Her book *Pregnancy and Childbirth*, first published in 1980, has sold approximately 1 million copies.

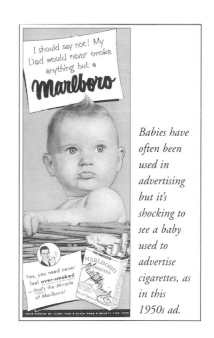

Babies have often been used in advertising but it's shocking to see a baby used to advertise cigarettes, as in this 1950s ad.

"By the time I conceived I was sure I wanted to give birth at home. My father was a GP in rural Herefordshire and I'd picked up a lot of understanding about childbirth matters and was able to put my case coherently and get my way, unlike many of the women I met during my pregnancy. Hospitals and nursing homes tended to have rigid policies which did not suit me, and I felt I would be disturbed by their lack of peace and quiet and privacy.

The infant Natural Childbirth Association, as the NCT was then, helped me contact two founder members, to whom I shall be forever grateful. Midwife Jill Tarttelin took everything in her stride and facilitated a memorable first experience of giving birth. I travelled to London, not so easy before motorways, to classes run by Betty Parsons, which were very different to those held at the local clinic. At the latter we were shown how to knit baby vests and taken through exercises by a physiotherapist – my back has been giving me trouble ever since! What they told us about childbirth I could have told them at the age of 10. At Betty's classes, on the other hand, we learned really useful relaxation and breathing techniques (before the advent of psychoprophylaxis) and talked about the things that really mattered to us, about the physical facts, the emotional aspects, and how we would cope and feel as parents.

One of the things I had to fight for was allowing my husband to be present at the birth. The doctor and district midwife were nonplussed and negative, and most of the people we knew found it a very kinky idea, so we learned to be discriminating about discussing the whole thing. Nowadays everyone talks openly about all aspects of childbirth. It's amazing to think that only 35 years ago the subject was mostly taboo. Anyway, Jill was happy to have Roy around if that was what suited us. She and I agreed that she would only call the doctor if she needed his expertise: she didn't, and Roy was an enormous support to me during the labour and delivery. We wouldn't have missed sharing the wonderful birth of our daughter for anything!"

ANN PROCTER ON THE BIRTH OF RUTH ON 15 APRIL 1959
AT HOME IN CAMBERLEY, SURREY.

"In those days you used to have an internal examination when you were 36 weeks pregnant to check your pelvic size. Women were always warned that they might have a show after it, but in my case it actually triggered labour. I stayed at home as long as I could and then we called an ambulance and I was taken off to hospital – in those days your husband just stayed at home and waited for news, he wasn't part of it at all.

Almost as soon as I arrived I was given pethidine, which was standard procedure in those days. I had two or three doses more over the next 24 hours, but the labour didn't move on properly – the baby's head wasn't coming down, and eventually they gave up on me delivering naturally and gave me a pre-med for a caesarean.

Just before they were about to start, though, they realised I was fully dilated, so they changed their minds and decided to use what we called 'high forceps'. They had to turn the baby round and pull him right out – he was still high up in the birth canal. I'm a midwife myself, and I know that in the same situation these days, you'd definitely have a section.

Anyway, in those days you were given a general anaesthetic for a complicated forceps delivery, and I suppose I was unconscious for half an hour or so. I've seen those kind of deliveries done – sometimes it looked like a scene from the last century, with the midwife holding on to the doctor because he was having to pull so hard to get the baby out.

When I came round, the baby had already been taken away. It seems quite shocking now, but it was par for the course in those days. He'd had a difficult start, and the drill in those days was what we called 'cot nursing', which meant the baby wouldn't be touched any more than was absolutely necessary for 48 hours. He was kept in the nursery, so I didn't even see him until he was nearly two days old. I remember they brought him along in his cot and left him by my bed just before the 48 hours was up. Of course I was desperate to look at him and hold him, so I picked him up and put him to the breast. He was ravenous – he'd only had a bottle of half-strength milk – and latched on straightaway. But then the curtains were pulled back and I got a real ticking off for getting him out of his cot too soon."

JEAN BIRD ON THE BIRTH OF JAMES ON 6 APRIL 1959 AT A MATERNITY HOSPITAL.

I was 33 when I had Karen. It was the first time I'd been pregnant, and at five months we moved house. When I went to see my new doctor, I was shocked to be told I'd have to give birth at home. There was no chance of getting a hospital bed at that stage. I was appalled – I felt hospital was the best place to have a baby. But my GP felt it was the ideal way to do it, and after talking to him and the district nurse I became more reconciled to the idea, though it definitely wouldn't have been my choice. It certainly didn't seem ideal – we had hardly any furniture, no heating and to make matters even worse, just before my due date we had a big freeze, and the water pipes froze.

By the time Karen arrived we had water again, but only cold, so my husband had to supervise the boiling of pans of water in the kitchen, just like in the films. I had the midwife and doctor, but I didn't have any pain-killers or anything. I'd read Grantly Dick-Read, and I believed in his method completely. It was a wonderful way to have a baby, I felt I was in control and didn't feel I was being pushed around or manipulated by the medical people in any way. My husband wasn't there, and I wouldn't have wanted him – I'm too private a person for that. But he was outside the door, and came in to see Karen as soon as she was born, which was lovely.

We didn't have a washing machine, so my husband had to take time off work to do all the washing and sort everything out after the delivery. He even had to burn the placenta, at the end of the garden! It was a very basic, no-frills way to have a baby, but none the worse for that. In many ways, despite my initial reservations, I felt very happy with the way things turned out.

EILEEN DUELL ON THE BIRTH OF KAREN ON 4 FEBRUARY 1956, AT HOME IN DENHAM, SOUTH BUCKS.

"*I was about five months pregnant by the time they discovered I was carrying twins. I can't remember exactly how I got suspicious that I might be, I suppose it just felt like a lot of baby in there. Anyway, my doctor obviously agreed, and he sent me along to the hospital for an X-ray, which was how they checked in those days. I remember I had to lie on my tummy on what looked like a sheet of black marble — it was quite difficult to lie like that by then, I was so big. I was a bit worried about having an X-ray when I was pregnant, but at that time you didn't feel you could question things. They were the professionals and they knew — you just took their word for it.*

Once twins had been diagnosed there wasn't anything special in the way of antenatal care, although our doctor knew us well and was always very helpful. When I was almost at term he passed me cycling down the road one day, and was obviously shocked to see me out and about looking so large. He decided I should be admitted to hospital to wait for the birth, which was terrible, I was in there for two weeks, and it was really dreary. I felt I was being held captive — it wasn't as though there was anything wrong with me or the babies.

Eventually they said I was overdue, and the labour was induced. I was taken to the theatre for that, and then put in a labour ward where I remember reading a rather good book and not really wanting to be disturbed. It didn't seem unduly painful. Finally I was moved to the delivery room, where a huge audience crowded in to see the babies born — I felt I should have been issued with an Equity card for the performance. There was the consultant, another doctor, some nurses, some nursing students, a sister tutor — they all wanted to see twins arrive. So I said if you're all going to see it I think I'd like to watch myself, and could I have a mirror. They obviously thought this was a bit of a lark, but they found one and I did see the babies come out, first Alexandra, and then about 30 minutes later Victoria arrived.

I was in hospital for about 14 days afterwards, which was the norm in those days. The babies weren't with me in the ward — they stayed in the nursery, and were brought in for feeds. I was breastfeeding, but although feeding twins was a bit tricky I don't remember getting much in the way of support; I was just shown what to do and left to get on with it. The nurses seemed very busy, they always appeared to be rushing off somewhere and never had time to chat.

Overall, my memory is of a system which was pretty bossy and seemed to owe a lot of its ideas to folklore. One thing which struck me was how I never met a midwife or doctor who I felt I really related to; I longed for the chance to build up a sense of trust with someone, but there was never any possibility of that. It was just like being a parcel on a production line, passed along regardless of who you were. I was ever so pleased to get home again, I can tell you."

*Denise Keir on the births of Alexandra and Victoria
on 16 October 1956 at a local hospital.*

In those days you didn't have much to do with the consultant, it was the midwives who ran the nursing homes, and they just called in a doctor if there was a serious problem. They had just started having relaxation classes when I was pregnant, so as well as antenatal clinics I went to these. They were very regimented, with breathing exercises and then you spent half an hour lying in the recovery position at the end. Husbands weren't involved at all, of course. I don't think the classes were very realistic — I remember the sister-tutor telling us it wouldn't be painful, just hard work.

I went two weeks overdue, so they decided to give me what they called a surgical induction. No one told me what was going to happen or what to expect, I was just put on the edge of a theatre bed and doused with hot and cold water and the doctor put his hand up with a pair of scissors and the water poured out into a bucket on the floor. I was terrified. I just didn't know what to expect, and no one told you. If you asked a question they'd just say something like 'you'll find out when you need to', or 'things will sort themselves out'.

Once in labour you just had to stay in bed — there was no question of walking around or anything like that. I was in labour for two days. They let my husband come in to sit with me, but as soon as they thought I was getting near delivery he was sent away, and I went to the delivery room. No-one asked what position felt most comfortable, the only way to have a baby was on your back, and you just had to put up with it.

I spent 14 days in the nursing home after Kerry's birth, but I hardly saw anything of her at all. She stayed in the nursery, and only came to me for four-hourly feeds. They left her for 20 minutes at a time, and after that back she went, whether she'd fed or not. Before the feed you'd get a bowl of water to wash your breasts, and another bowl to wash them again afterwards. We also had to put lanolin and friar's balsam on our breasts, and to bind them tightly with a towel-like bandage between feeds.

You weren't allowed to do anything for yourself in the nursing home. They were terrified of infections getting to the babies, and we weren't allowed to change our own sanitary towels for fear that we'd somehow pass something on to the baby. No one but your husband could visit the baby, and even he needed permission from the midwife. It wasn't until Kerry came home at two weeks that her grandparents were able to meet her.

JOAN CHILDS ON THE BIRTH OF DAUGHTER KERRY
AT A NURSING HOME ON 20 APRIL 1957.

"I was very fortunate because we had a private maternity nurse, who came to live with us from the time I went into labour until about three weeks later. She was a midwife in her seventies, a very small woman who always wore her full uniform when looking after me or the baby. This consisted of a starched white collar and cuffs, white dress, long black cape and a black-frilled bonnet tied underneath her chin.

I had a false alarm, so Nurse, as we always called her, was already in residence, sharing my older daughter's bedroom, when I started having contractions again. My husband went to knock on her door, and she apparently appeared in a dressing-gown with her hair loose, but before coming in to see me she put her hair up and her uniform on!

During the delivery itself there were two doctors present so Nurse was a bit in the background, but once Stephanie arrived she took over the reins and ran the household. She believed strongly in routine, and kept religiously to it; baby was brought in for four-hourly feeds, and walks in the park were at 2pm each day, whatever the weather, for at least half an hour. When my husband came home from work, she always brought Stephanie in to him for 20 minutes of cuddles; I suppose you would call it 'bonding' nowadays. He once asked her how long she would let a baby cry for, and she replied: 'Until you can stand it no longer'.

Nurse had firm and old-fashioned ideas, but she wasn't a forbidding person; to me, she seemed kindness itself. I spent the first 10 days confined to bed, and whenever my breasts got sore she would massage them with olive oil, which helped a lot. We missed her when she left, but by then I'd had a really good rest and was able to take over. She'd been with us for just about four weeks, I think, and her final bill was £20."

TERESA CURTIS ON THE BIRTH OF STEPHANIE
AT HOME IN LUTON, BEDFORDSHIRE, ON 26 DECEMBER 1956.

CHAPTER 3

1960ˢ
Gadgets and Gimmicks

The 1960s was the decade with a gadget for everything, and pregnancy was no exception. Whether you were feeling a bit peaky, or your baby seemed a bit on the small side, or your blood pressure was up a bit … the solution was close at hand, in the shape of the extraordinary Heynes Decompression Chair. This contraption, developed in the 1950s, was, by the mid-1960s, the cure-all for many a pregnancy complaint, and some even reckoned it helped produce more intelligent babies. Dr Joan Gomez, writing in *Mother and Baby* in July 1966, gave this colourful description of how the treatment worked:

'The mother sits in what feels like a comfortable armchair, and a plastic cover, pink candy-striped, since pregnancy is a cheerful affair, is zipped up to her shoulders. A vacuum pump controlled by the mother herself, regulates the pressure inside the suit. The idea is that a partial vacuum in the area round the womb produces a better flow of blood into it, bringing more oxygen to the placenta. At the same time the wall of the womb itself is encouraged to expand, and the placenta attached to it is also gently stretched. The bigger the placenta, like the bigger the dinner plate, the more it can provide in nourishment and oxygen, particularly since it now has a better supply of blood.'

In the delivery room, meanwhile, there was excitement about other machines – the new partograms

"In those days you got a maternity grant of £14 for general expenses, plus a £6 'home confinement grant' if the baby was born at home."

The Heynes Decompression Chair was considered a cure-all for many a pregnancy complaint. Some thought it increased the oxygen supply to the baby.

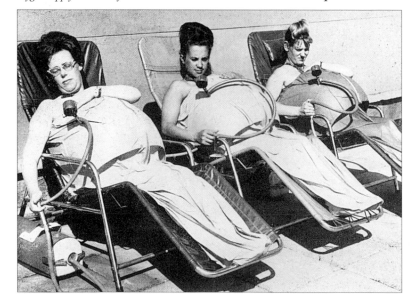

which measured contractions, and cardiotographs which checked the fetal heart rate. Fetal monitoring was further enhanced by the development of a way of taking a blood sample from the baby's scalp during labour, to check its oxygen level. Meanwhile rhesus disease, a big concern among mothers-to-be in the 1960s because it had only recently been properly identified, was the subject of intensive research, and by the end of the decade doctors were able to test whether a baby was affected by drawing off a sample of amniotic fluid from a mother known to be at risk. In some cases, they were even transfusing a baby's whole blood supply before birth.

All this helped add to the general 1960s perception that having a baby, like everything else, was improving all the time. While Prime Minister Harold Macmillan was telling the nation they'd never had it so good, *Mother and Baby* readers (March 1967) were being assured: 'Of course you're glad to be a mother. Be glad it's now.' Advances in childbirth were, the magazine assured them, 'Nearly all for the better', and included:

> 'New, brighter buildings with smaller 4-8 bed wards.
> More rooming-in of babies with their mothers.
> Special units for premature babies.
> 'Flying squads', medical/obstetrical teams on tap to help mothers at home needing special care.
> The 48-hour mini-stay in hospital, combining maximum safety for the delivery with the happiness of minimum separation from home and husband.
> GP Units, where family doctors can look after their own patients: usually you're home 24 hours after the birth.
> Fathers being allowed to share, especially in the slow waiting time of the first stage … '

Certainly, the experience of having a baby was improving for women in some ways. The length of stay in hospital was definitely getting shorter – down from 12 days in 1955 to eight days in 1968 if you were under a consultant's care, and from 11 days to about seven if your GP was managing your case. This reduction was partly a spin-off from the *Cranbrook Report*'s recommendation to increase the number of deliveries taking place in an institution: the target figure of 70% was reached in 1964 and went on rising to reach 80.6% by 1968. But the rise in hospital deliveries was not achieved

---

ERNA WRIGHT

An NCT antenatal teacher who introduced to British women an idea which had been originated in France by an obstetrician named Lamaze, that they could cope better with the pain of childbirth if they learnt a system of breathing exercises. Her book *The New Childbirth* was a best-seller in the 1960s.

"We got a washing machine for the first time in the 1960s, and everything seemed much easier after that. My next baby was a complete doddle."

Mother and Baby *magazine, launched in 1956 was soon joined in the 1960s by* Parents *Magazine.*

DR BENJAMIN SPOCK

The paediatrician whose comprehensive and down-to-earth *Common Sense Book of Baby and Child Care* is a bestseller outsold only by the Bible.

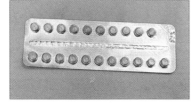

The contraceptive pill, licensed during the 1960s, enabled women to take control of their own bodies and family planning became much more reliable, leading to smaller families.

Princess Alexandra with her husband and children before the christening of the youngest member, Marina Ogilvy. Angus Ogilvy's presence at the birth of his son James attracted particular press attention, and gave a boost to the campaign to allow partners to be present at the birth of their babies.

due to an increased number of beds available; it was because women were being processed through the system quicker, thus freeing beds for new admissions.

On the labour wards, fathers were beginning to be tolerated. But it was a slow process. On 1 June 1964 *The Times* noted that:

> *'A few hospitals are beginning to encourage husbands; some can be persuaded to let a husband in; the majority cling to the view that a man's place is pacing the waiting room and justify their attitude with excuses like "There's no room for a man here" or, more ingeniously, "There's no lavatory for them."'*

The campaign to admit fathers to the delivery room was led from the coal face, by men who wanted to be there and by women who felt they needed the support and considered the birth of a child an experience a couple ought to share. Antenatal teachers, especially NCT ones, encouraged the trend enthusiastically, some even joking to their classes that the men should go armed with handcuffs, so they could chain themselves to the sink if anyone tried to eject them from the room. (This had actually happened in a much-publicised case in Chicago, when a husband determined to attend his baby's birth handcuffed himself to the delivery table so he could not be dragged away.)

Early in 1964 the campaign got a fillip with the news that Angus Ogilvy, husband of Princess Alexandra, had been in the delivery room for the arrival of their son, James. Royal acceptance of the trend was an important stamp of approval, and from that time on the presence of the father was considered, if rather unorthodox, then at least no longer quirky. All this assumed, of course, that the father was the husband: a boyfriend would have been *persona non grata*, certainly not welcome in the delivery room and only just about tolerated as a visitor.

But though doctors and midwives became gradually more amenable, it wasn't necessarily out of the best of motives. In an article in *Parents* magazine in May 1963, Elizabeth Dixon describes how, during her labour, the Sister on duty explained to her that women were 'more co-operative patients if their husbands were there – they want to impress them, it puts them on their mettle.' And it solved hospital staffing shortages, she added wryly.

Perhaps more worryingly, where fathers were welcomed into the delivery room they tended to be fussed over almost as much as the baby, often to the detriment of the mother. Jacqueline Wilson, writing in *Mother and Baby* in December 1967, enthused about her husband's presence at the birth of their daughter, but added a cautionary caveat. 'He was marvellous and I really don't know what I would have done without him. The moment of birth is the deepest emotional experience a man and wife can share and it meant so much to both of us. But I don't think I would have been human if I hadn't felt a pinprick of annoyance when all the nurses clustered around him after Emma was born and breathlessly congratulated him for being so helpful, encouraging and kind. I waited for my share of the congratulations but all I got was: "You didn't half make a dreadful fuss … "'

For some diehards, though, the whole idea of husbands being there remained anathema. Mrs J Banstead of Accrington summed up her feelings with this letter to *Mother and Baby* in June 1965:

'I simply do not understand some women wishing to have their husbands present at the actual birth of a baby. One's whole instinct I find is to be quiet and alone and with only a doctor or midwife present. Let us face facts – birth is ugly, messy and usually painful and one does not want to be watched at such a time. Men are usually far more squeamish than women about pain and I should have thought a sensitive husband having once witnessed his wife in this condition would never want her to have another child.'

Pregnancy and babies were much in the news in 1964, when four members of the Royal Family, all supporters of natural childbirth, were expecting. More royal babies were born throughout the decade. The Duchess of Kent with Lady Helen Windsor in 1964 (top picture), and Princess Margaret (bottom picture) with Viscount Linley, born in 1961.

Meanwhile, away from the interminable queues at antenatal clinics, which women were often forced to endure in hospital gowns, holding bottles of urine and with their knickers in a plastic bag, pregnancy was actually becoming quite fashionable. This was partly because of the rash of Royal mothers in 1964, dubbed 'Royal Baby Year' by the media. The Queen, Princess Margaret, the Duchess of Kent and Princess Alexandra were all

WHAT ELSE HAPPENED IN THE 1960s?

- The Pill became available on the NHS

- The Profumo affair shocked the nation

- The Great Train Robbers struck

- Beatlemania swept the country, and mods and rockers clashed on the beaches

- Winston Churchill died, aged 91

- The death penalty was abolished in Britain

- Abortion became legal.

Elvis Presley and his wife Priscilla opted for a hospital delivery. On 10 February 1968 the new father collected his wife and daughter, Lisa Marie, from the Baptist Hospital at Memphis, Tennessee.

expecting, and the papers were full of articles about eating the right foods during pregnancy and how to kit out a nursery fit for a prince. The Royals also turned out to be keen natural childbirth followers, and several were 'Betty P girls', as the midwives dubbed them, graduates of the Betty Parsons antenatal school. Mrs Parsons, by now well-established as the top people's childbirth guru, came with the seal of approval of the Queen's gynaecologist Sir John Peel, and her catchphrase 'Drop shoulders, breathe out gently, pause and let your breath come' was typical of her relaxation-centred approach.

Relaxation had become the key word in antenatal classes by the early 1960s. But while some, like Betty Parsons, realised that it was part of a bigger jigsaw of coping strategies for labour, others believed it was simply all that mattered. Some books suggested ways of learning to relax your body completely with the aim of lying relaxed on the floor during the first stage of labour. The trouble was, as the authors usually went on to acknowledge, relaxing and having beautiful thoughts wasn't normally enough when the contractions got stronger, so women who'd learned to cope with the early stages would be advised to accept pain-relieving drugs for the rest of labour. What pregnant women needed was a strategy to take them through the whole process of having a baby, and the person who delivered this most spectacularly was NCT antenatal teacher Erna Wright, whose book *The New Childbirth* had been reprinted many times by the end of the decade, and continued to have a strong following right through the 1970s.

Wright's system was known as psychoprophylaxis, a made-up word, as she herself said, which basically meant brain-washing. Her system was based on breathing techniques and diversion tactics which could be learned beforehand so they were almost automatic by delivery day. Learning to give birth was, Mrs Wright reckoned, 'Like learning any other skill: learning to ride a bicycle, drive a car, play a musical instrument, operate a knitting-machine or indeed learning to read and write'. What mattered most was mastering

THE THALIDOMIDE TRAGEDY

It began as a trickle, but it quickly became a flood. And the papers, in the early 1960s, were full of it – a story to put the fear of God into every pregnant woman in Britain.

The story was, of course, thalidomide, a drug first marketed in 1957 for nervous tension, migraine headaches and, most tragically of all, morning sickness. Ironically, it was initially considered an extremely safe preparation – unlike other sedatives, massive doses were not lethal and it was thought to pose no suicide threat.

But by 1961, the press had begun to notice what was becoming an epidemic of severely malformed babies. It wasn't only here – babies in Germany and Australia, other countries where thalidomide was licensed, were similarly affected. As it turned out, the drug that had seemed so safe was interfering with the growth of babies in the womb, probably by targeting the developing blood vessels and stunting normal growth. Babies were born with varying degrees of deformities of the limbs, ears, eyes and internal organs – the most severe impairment was phocomelia, in which the long bones of the limbs are misshapen and hands and feet arise almost straight from the trunk.

Midwives and obstetricians, like everyone else, were horrified by what was happening. As a result, they often found themselves ill-equipped to deal with the birth of a baby affected by thalidomide. Many parents had their babies hustled off moments after the delivery, and were not told for many hours what was wrong. One father was told he couldn't see his son because the child had no head. Another was told it would be best if his wife didn't see their daughter, as she would surely die within hours.

In fact, that baby – and 457 others in Britain – survived to adulthood. The fear of whether thalidomide would go on to affect another generation seemed disproved when many went on to produce perfectly-formed children of their own. More recently, though, it became clear that eight out of 400 or so babies of original thalidomide victims have themselves suffered from limb or other abnormalities. Can the drug have affected gene composition as well as limbs and bodies? Only time, it seems, will tell.

Ironically, Distaval – alias thalidomide – was marketed as being a safe drug for mothers to take because their children were unlikely to harm themselves if they accidentally swallowed the pills.

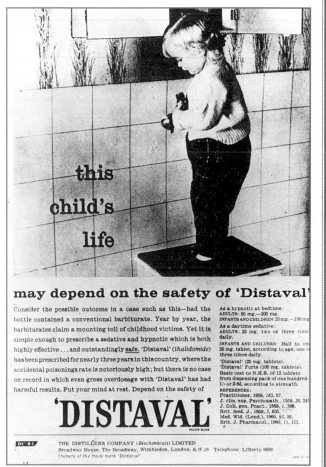

this
child's
life

may depend on the safety of 'Distaval'

Consider the possible outcome in a case such as this—had the bottle contained a conventional barbiturate. Year by year, the barbiturates claim a mounting toll of childhood victims. Yet it is simple enough to prescribe a sedative and hypnotic which is both highly effective . . . and outstandingly <u>safe</u>. 'Distaval' (*thalidomide*) has been prescribed for nearly three years in this country, where the accidental poisonings rate is notoriously high; but there is no case on record in which even gross overdosage with 'Distaval' has had harmful results. Put your mind at rest. Depend on the safety of

As a hypnotic at bedtime:
ADULTS: 50 mg.—200 mg.
INFANTS AND CHILDREN: 25 mg.—100 mg.
As a daytime sedative:
ADULTS: 25 mg, two or three times daily.
INFANTS AND CHILDREN: Half to one 25 mg. tablet, according to age, one to three times daily.
'Distaval' (25 mg. tablets).
'Distaval' Forte (100 mg. tablets).
Basic cost to N.H.S. of 12 tablets from dispensing pack of one hundred, 1/- or 2/8d. according to strength.
REFERENCES:
Practitioner, 1959, *183*, 57.
J. clin. exp. Psychopath., 1959, *20*, 241.
J. Coll. gen. Pract., 1958, *1*, 398.
Brit. med. J., 1959, *2*, 635.
Med. Wld. (Lond.), 1960, *93*, 26.
Brit. J. Pharmacol., 1960, *15*, 111.

'DISTAVAL'
TRADE MARK

THE DISTILLERS COMPANY (*Biochemicals*) LIMITED
Broadway House, The Broadway, Wimbledon, London, S.W.19   Telephone: LIBerty 6600
Owners of the trade mark 'Distaval'

"Children were never allowed in maternity wards so there was no chance for my three older ones to see their new brother until he was ten days old – and they missed me terribly at home."

TOP 20 *Names of the 1960s*	
BOYS	**G**IRLS
Paul	Trac(e)y
David	Deborah
Andrew	Julie
Stephen	Karen
Mark	Susan
Michael	Alison
Ian	Jacqueline
Gary	Helen
Robert	Amanda
Richard	Sharon

SOURCE: *THE GUINNESS BOOK OF NAMES*, 7TH EDITION

"My doctor told me marital relations, as he put it, were out for the last three months of my pregnancy – he said germs could be introduced into the vagina that way."

four levels of breathing, labelled A to D, which you were then advised to think of 'as the four gears in your car … It will help you appreciate all the more, how important it is to "change gear" quickly and smoothly'. The idea was that you could 'change gear' with your breathing to help you cope as the contractions became stronger.

One of the trademarks of Wright's method was her advice to sing during contractions to blot out the pain. She urged her readers to 'choose a song, which you like and of which you know the words. Don't choose a nursery-song because this is too simple. Rather find a pop-song or some other one you are fond of, which also has a good rollicking rhythm. Now sing the song in your head, mime it with your lips, and tap the rhythm with your fingers on the table, or on your lap. Always use the same song when practising and also later during labour – make it *your* song. Particularly, exaggerate the miming with your lips, because this activity of the muscles surrounding the mouth helps a great deal when you are trying to maintain control over your muscles.' So it was that a generation was born while mum (and dad, for his presence was integral to the psychoprophylaxic method) belted out the latest Beatles hit, much to the amusement of many a delivery room team.

Painless childbirth was a major theme in the magazines and baby books of the 1960s. For some, like Erna Wright, it was simply an unacknowledged fact – she was convinced that 35% of women who had been through her classes could achieve a pain-free labour. For others, childbirth without pain was something to strive for by any means possible – many midwives and obstetricians believed that by now, the middle of the 20th century, civilised society should have come up with an answer to suffering in labour. But most found it hard to believe that a woman's own resources, properly channelled, could really be the answer, and as the decade wore on drugs became more and more routine in labour – by 1970, 97% of women were having some form of analgesia.

Many were getting more than one drug, for the usual course was to give tranquillisers or sleeping pills in early labour; pethidine when the contractions were more established; and gas and air or trilene once the cervix was well dilated. Books and magazines gave glib assurances that the drugs couldn't harm the baby, but the amounts of pethidine injected were often very high, much higher than would be given today. Worse, the drugs were frequently administered without the consent or even understanding of the woman concerned: the midwife would cheerily announce it was 'time for your smarties', or you'd feel a needle in your thigh before you realised what was going on, and be told it was 'just a little something to help with the pain'.

As Sheila Kitzinger pointed out in *The Experience of Childbirth*, administering dose after dose of drugs meant an almost inevitable loss of control for the woman in labour, so that those who had faithfully attended their antenatal classes and practised their breathing and relaxation exercises were suddenly, on the day it really mattered, all at sea. Drugs had, and clearly still have, their place in the delivery room, but resorting to them too quickly wasn't necessarily doing a mother-to-be any favours, and could lead to a lengthier labour and perhaps a forceps delivery. What was more, drugs would certainly cause a loss of awareness in a woman who quite possibly wanted to be mentally alert when her baby came into the world.

But individual wishes were, as Dr John Gibbens noted in *The Care of Young Babies*, often overlooked. 'Recently the papers have been full of criticism of maternity hospitals, full of their shortcomings,' he wrote. 'While most of them agree that the obstetric care is as good as ever, they complain bitterly that mothers are treated harshly and unsympathetically, "like sausages in a machine", without any proper thought for their emotional problems.' And even if you didn't have problems you might have preferences, but these often just weren't taken on board by the 1960s system.

By 1965, birth in hospital had become very medicalised. Joan Neilson, writing in *Mother and Baby* in June of that year, gives a description of an experience that was by now clinical, even cold:

'At the beginning of the second stage you will be taken to the labour room … This is a small bare room with a high bed in it where your baby will be born in aseptic conditions. The doctor and midwife will don gowns and masks just as for a surgical operation … The obstetric bed is steel based and provides good support for you in the pushing stage. You will be placed on your back,

> *Breastfeeding was very unfashionable in the 1960s. I fed my babies myself, but never in public. And a lot of my middle-class friends secretly thought it reflected my working-class roots, I'm sure.*

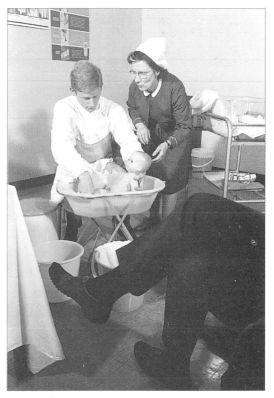

Fathers became more involved in the birth of their children, and they slowly began to take on some of the practical aspects of their care. In 1968 Margate Hospital in Kent set up preparation for parenthood classes for men. Here an expectant father learns the correct bathing technique with the help of a life-sized baby doll.

Spring/Summer 1967   mothercare

Everything for the mother-to-be and her baby

Mothercare appeared in the High Street in the 1960s, reflecting the spirit of an age in which parents wanted new things for new babies and were no longer content with hand-me-downs. Featured in the catalogue for spring and summer of 1967 was the first Babystretch, which freed both mother and infant from the tedium and discomfort of buttons and patent fasteners.

thighs wide apart and your legs up in the air supported by two leather stirrups. This is called the lithotomy position and is used to enable whoever is delivering you to control the descent of your baby's head through the birth canal. You will, of course, be draped in sterile towels and you will find the position quite suitable for the hard work you have to do.'

At home, things could still be different: more informal, more friendly, with more involvement from your partner and a bit more say in what went on. The Home Help service continued to thrive through the 1960s, in most areas at least. Jeanne Treasure, writing in *Parents* in March 1961, testified to the remarkable efficiency of an organisation that really transformed the whole experience of being at home with a newborn baby:

'We were fortunate in that Louise came punctually on the afternoon of the Sunday we expected her … My husband phoned the Home Help office first thing next morning and, in less than half an hour, a cheerful, very capable lady had come to take over all the jobs which I should normally have been doing. She was with us for two weeks, from 8.30 in the morning until 4 in the afternoon and this cost us just under £7 for the fortnight.'

But despite this excellent domestic support, and the existence of a reliable obstetric flying squad in most areas, home birth was seen by a growing number of people as very much second best. Since the birth rate continued to rise throughout the decade, there was pressure on beds, and the books and magazines of the time were full of exhortations to 'book early, or you may be disappointed' if you wanted a hospital delivery. If you left it much later than around the time when your second period would have been due, you might miss out, in which case you could only get an 'emergency bed' in hospital if your medical condition dictated.

But was hospital the best place? The obstetricians spent

the decade revising their views on which women were 'suitable' candidates for home birth, but by 1965 most GPs agreed that those expecting first babies, those over 35, and those who already had any previous obstetric complications should automatically go into hospital. Few people seemed to question the trend towards 100% hospital delivery, which by 1970 had become adopted as official government policy. Most writers agreed that home was a more relaxed and sociable environment for birth, and helped forge better family relationships, but most seemed to agree, reluctantly, that giving it up was simply the price mothers had to pay for 'safer', 'healthier' childbirth. Quite why it was *necessarily* safer or healthier, not many people had yet thought to question.

But wherever you actually gave birth, the business of having a baby was becoming much more acquisitive throughout the 1960s. No longer was it sufficient, as it had been in the still war-battered 1950s, to dust down the family cot and wheel out your parents' old pram – this was the decade when mum and dad became consumers.

Everything was to be brand new and shop-bought for Son (or Daughter) of the 1960s – it was, after all, the start of a new age, and the musty old items of years gone by were no longer seen as relevant or good enough. Babyhood was reinvented that decade, and top of the list of new priorities was buying the right goods. Mothercare, Britain's first specialist mother-to-be and new mother retailer, opened its doors in Kingston-upon-Thames in September 1961, and by the end of the decade it had more than 100 thriving stores throughout Britain.

Even in the Mothercare catalogue the father's role was still seen as rather removed from the practical aspects of parenting.

'*During the last five years the nursery world has expanded considerably,*' *gushed* Mother and Baby *in March 1964.* '*There is a wonderful choice range to satisfy every mother's taste, whether she enjoys the traditional daintiness of frills and lace which go with a new baby or the modern practicality of utilitarian time and labour savers. A visit to a nursery or pram shop today can be quite an awe-inspiring experience. Almost too wide a choice of goods are displayed for one to take in all at once.*'

The fashion world, too, was waking up to the fact that mums-to-be liked to look good and might not – shock horror – want to actually hide that bump. Until now, clothing yourself during pregnancy had been a question of wearing your biggest, baggiest items until they literally wouldn't do up, and then – if you absolutely had to – going out to buy a bigger version of the things you usually wore. But by the mid-1960s women's magazines regularly ran fashion spreads on maternity clothes, featuring pictures of oh-so elegant models, made up to the nines and with hair immaculately beehived, wearing shorter-than-short dresses cut to flatter a growing tum. Many 1960s fashions lent themselves quite well to adaptation for pregnant women: smocked tops, waistless dresses which gathered below the bust and hung loose to the knee, and flowing trouser suits.

"The big issue for us in the NCT in the 1960s was getting men into the delivery rooms. I remember we used to go to see obstetricians who were being sticky about it and refusing to let husbands in, and we'd tell them our point of view and say it was what women wanted, and that we felt it made for a better start to family life. Some of them were very strongly against it – I remember one obstetrician who looked at me very disapprovingly across his desk and said childbirth was revolting, and that he considered it almost pornographic to allow partners into a delivery room. He said it was a dirty business, and men shouldn't be subjected to it."
ROSALEEN MANSFIELD,
NCT MEMBER SINCE THE 1950s

"Top of the babies' fashion stakes were matinée jackets, while for toddlers Chilprufe tunics and cardigans were all the rage."

HAVE BUGGY, WILL TRAVEL

In 1965 a revolution in baby transport was signalled by the patenting by Maclaren Ltd of the umbrella-fold baby buggy. It was designed by a retired aeronautical engineer, Owen Finlay Maclaren, whose daughter lived in America and needed a small lightweight pushchair to use when bringing her children home by plane. He relied on his knowledge of the complex folding of load-bearing structures gained in the design of aeroplanes. Commercial sales began in February 1967. Conventional pushchair design had been turned upside down, and the traditional pram became increasingly a rarity on the streets.

"I was about five months pregnant, and everything seemed to be going well. But then a routine check at the antenatal clinic showed I had toxaemia, and I was sent straight home and put on bed-rest. I was very scared, as my cousin had died of toxaemia just six months before – although even in those days, that was rare.

The midwife and doctor came to check my blood pressure daily, and they were very strict about me staying in bed. I could only get up to use the toilet, although I was allowed one day to go Christmas shopping, and to spend time up with the family on Christmas Day.

I'd decided on a home birth, and despite the problems the midwives and doctor were agreeable – they all lived nearby and could get to my home easily. I went 20 days overdue, and in the end they broke my waters to get labour going. But things didn't progress – I was in labour for three days, and as the baby was a brow presentation with the forehead first, he just couldn't get down the birth canal. In the end the doctor gave me morphine, and we decided I'd better get to hospital.

As luck would have it there was a pea-soup fog that night – the ambulance that took me to hospital had to have a police escort. It was a horrendous journey lasting one hour – I was squashed into the ambulance with a midwife and a doctor and my husband and my mother.

When we finally arrived, the consultant took one look at me and said it would have to be a caesarean. I told him he could cut me in half if he wanted, by that stage, I was past caring.

But the worst thing of all was still to come. Because I was going to have a general anaesthetic, I had to have my stomach pumped. Unfortunately, though, the midwife tried to do it too quickly and put the tube down my windpipe instead of my oesophagus. I could have done without that, as you can imagine.

The next thing I remember is coming round after the operation. I had a vague recollection of having seen the baby in the theatre, but I couldn't be sure. Anyway, they told me I had a boy and he was doing fine in Special Care, but I didn't believe them – I was convinced the baby was dead. I got so upset about it that a medical student took pity on me and 'borrowed' Timothy from the Special Care nursery for a few minutes so I could have a peep. He came dashing in with him, because he would have got into trouble if anyone had found out. But I'll never forget that kindness. I started to recover myself once I knew Timothy was alright."

JEAN DERRICK ON THE BIRTH OF TIMOTHY
AT A HOSPITAL IN THE WEST COUNTRY ON 26 JANUARY 1960.

"My doctor was quite elderly, and I don't think he was very clued up in obstetrics. At one stage when he was examining me he said he could hear two heartbeats, but I just wrote it off as a mistake.

I'd had my first two children at home, and intended to be at home for this one. But just before the due date, I started bleeding. The midwife and doctor were worried, so they called an ambulance and off I went, at 3am, to hospital.

I remember that I didn't feel any pain at all during the labour, I just felt numb. But that didn't stop them giving me pethidine, which made me feel awful and really was quite unnecessary. But I wasn't asked whether I wanted it, they just gave me the injection as a matter of course.

I was in labour for about 15 hours before Gifford was born. The delivery was quite difficult, and while they were checking him over they started pummelling my stomach to get the afterbirth delivered, when suddenly the midwife announced: 'There's another one in here'. And so there was – she was born about ten minutes later. After she arrived they spent a lot of time trying to decide whether there was a third baby – I remember lying there and thinking oh no, surely not.

In fact I was quite relieved to know I'd been carrying twins, because I'd been very large when I was pregnant and it did worry me slightly that there was something wrong with the baby. In fact the twins were very large: 6lb 15oz and 7lb 4oz – they held the record for the second largest twins born in Winchester for some years.

Having undiagnosed twins certainly wasn't that unusual in the 1960s, but even then I think you did usually find out beforehand. I know the Sister on the postnatal ward felt a bit sorry for me that I hadn't known. But it was fine – I'd always thought three would be an awkward number of children, so in many ways having four was preferable.

Being in hospital for 12 days after the birth, though, was an awful experience. They'd started leaving babies by their mothers' beds by then, so of course I had my two next to me. My milk didn't come in properly, so I was giving them bottles and having to get up myself in the night to prepare them. It was hard work straight after the delivery, and made me realise how unsuitable hospital birth is. If I'd been at home, I'd have had my husband and family to support me. I'm sure you get more help if you have twins in hospital these days, but at that stage they just weren't geared up for them."

JULIA MOSELEY ON THE BIRTH OF GIFFORD AND SHARON
ON 5 NOVEMBER 1962 AT A DISTRICT HOSPITAL.

"I had five miscarriages, and it seemed as though we were never going to have a baby. So when a friend said she knew someone looking for adoptive parents for a baby who was on the way, we jumped at the chance. We did it all legally, of course, and got Karen when she was just seven days old. The same day, I discovered I was pregnant again. Of course I was delighted, but I didn't really expect it would work out – every month I was waiting for the miscarriage to happen. I couldn't believe it when I got to nine months and there really was still a baby on the way.

It was hard work, of course, being pregnant when I already had such a young baby to care for, but I managed. I thought how nice it would be for the two of them to grow up so close in age. The pregnancy seemed quite normal, no cause for concern at all. Then at the end I went overdue, and after a week they took me into hospital to induce me. But I think the threat of that must have got to me, because my labour started the night before they were going to start it anyway.

It wasn't a long labour – the pain started at about 9am and it was all over by midday. I don't remember a lot about the actual birth, I know they said they were going to have to cut me to get the baby out. But after she was born there was no noise or anything. That's what I remember, the quiet. I suppose it must have been a few minutes before they told me that the baby was dead, and then they gave me an injection to help me sleep.

When I came round I was in a private ward – obviously they weren't going to put me in with all the other women who had babies. Everyone tried to be as kind as possible, of course, the doctor came to see me and told me the baby had died of asphyxia. But he didn't give me many details, I still don't know whether she ever breathed, or whether she was already dead. I know there was a heartbeat during the labour, because I remember them checking for that.

I never saw my baby. It wasn't suggested that I should, and I'd never have thought to ask to – it just wasn't done in those days. I don't know what happened to her body. My husband might have been told, I know he had to sort out various things, but we never really spoke about it. I know he had to register her birth – he gave her the name we'd already chosen if we had a little girl, which was Sian.

Everyone tried to be sympathetic, but what I remember most was that no one would talk to me about it, and I did need to talk. There was no counselling or anything like that – you just got on with it in those days. But it was hard. The hardest bit of all, I think, was walking out of that hospital with empty arms – that really brought it home. About three weeks after the birth I had a really bad turn, lots of shaking fits and so on, I suppose it was the grief welling up inside. Having Karen helped a lot, of course, but you never quite get over it. I still think of Sian sometimes."

DOREEN VICKERS ON THE BIRTH OF SIAN ON 16 MARCH 1961
AT A HOSPITAL IN THE HOME COUNTIES.

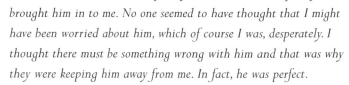

My husband and I are both wheelchair-users; I had polio at the age of 16 and am paralysed from the chest down. We were delighted when we found out I was pregnant, but no one I encountered during my visits to the antenatal clinic seemed remotely joyful or enthusiastic about what we were doing. My consultant was extremely dismissive — I was obviously concerned about how the birth would be and so on, but she just wouldn't discuss it at all. I told her I'd had a spinal fusion because of my polio, which meant my spinal cord had been fused together, but she said that wouldn't affect my ability to give birth at all.

I was already in hospital when my waters broke, and I was sent straight to the delivery ward as the consultant had said I could expect a very quick labour. But two days later nothing had happened, and I was in a lot of pain. Eventually a registrar came in and examined me, and asked what the scar was on my back. When I said it was a spinal fusion he was shocked: 'You'll never have your baby naturally in a month of Sundays if you've had a spinal fusion,' he said. 'Why didn't you tell us before?'

Jeremy was born by caesarean later that day — they didn't even bother to tell Andrew, my husband, what was happening. I was taken back to a room on my own and left there — no one suggested taking me to see the baby, who was in an incubator because he'd become distressed during the long labour. It wasn't until three days later that I got to see Jeremy — the consultant asked me why I wasn't eating, and I said I was too worried about my baby to eat. So eventually they

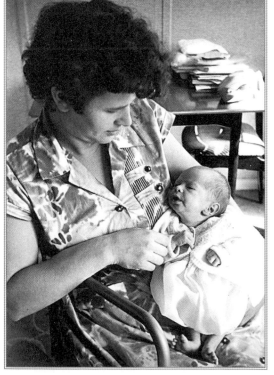

brought him in to me. No one seemed to have thought that I might have been worried about him, which of course I was, desperately. I thought there must be something wrong with him and that was why they were keeping him away from me. In fact, he was perfect.

Looking back, what I remember most about my pregnancy and Jeremy's birth was the complete lack of support and friendliness. Even after he was born, I don't remember anyone saying isn't this great, you've got a lovely baby. They just said things like 'but however will you cope?' Even after 33 years, it can still make me angry to think about it. But the wonderful joy of having a child of our own, of course, transcended all the hurt and anger.

NANCY ROBERTSON ON THE BIRTH OF HER SON JEREMY
AT A LONDON HOSPITAL ON 21 AUGUST 1962.

I was just 19 years old, and unmarried, when I got pregnant with Lucy. It wasn't the thing to do in those days, of course, and I was sent off to stay at an unmarried mothers' hostel in South London. When I went into labour they called an ambulance to take me to a local hospital – I remember it all seemed very exciting. When I got there I had to go through all the rigmarole of being shaved and being given an enema, and then I was put to bed in the labour ward. I had pethidine, so the memory is a bit hazy, but I remember being in a huge long Victorian ward – in bed, of course – with moans and groans and a few shrieks going on around me. The midwives came to check on you from time to time, but essentially you were on your own. It was pretty lonely, and I was there for about 18 hours.

The atmosphere was very much that you did as you were told and had to ask if you wanted to do anything. I wanted to go to the loo, and I waited for someone to come along so I could ask permission. But no one came, and I got desperate, so off I went. While I was there I started to get the urge to push, so I called for someone and they got me onto a trolley and took me to the delivery room. It was just like an operating theatre – a cold, clinical room with a high bed and stirrups.

In the delivery room everyone was quite encouraging and supportive. I don't really remember any negative remarks about my being an unmarried mother, though I was very definitely always referred to as Mrs Hunt. I gave birth lying on my back, though my head was propped up and I did catch sight of her being born. Afterwards they gave her to me to hold while I was being stitched, which was lovely.

I was the only breastfeeding mother on the postnatal ward. I expect they thought it was just another odd thing about me, as I was a bit unusual anyway, being younger than everyone else and unmarried. I stayed in for about five days – Lucy was with me in the ward during the day and in the nursery at night and, oddly, during general visiting hours. As far as I remember, the only way to show your baby off to your relatives and friends was to go to the nursery and point her out through the glass.

SALLY JONES ON THE BIRTH OF LUCY ON 26 JUNE 1966 AT A HOSPITAL IN WEST LONDON.

"It was the summer of 1962, and the papers were full of stories about thalidomide babies. I was expecting my first baby, so naturally I was very interested in it all. I remember discussing it with a friend one day, who was also pregnant. She said if she knew she was having an affected baby she'd have an abortion, but I said no, I couldn't do that.

Simone was a breech birth, so I was taken into hospital and induced. I had gas and air during the delivery, so I was a bit woozy. But I remember there were lots of medical people in the room, and I just had this feeling something was wrong after she was born. They kept trying to put the mask over my face so I couldn't ask anything or see what was going on. And then a doctor came quite close to me and asked had I taken any drugs during my pregnancy? And then I knew, I just knew, that I'd had one of those babies.

They showed Simone to me very briefly in the delivery room, but I only saw her face as she was wrapped in a shawl. And I remember thinking, well, she's a pretty little thing, whatever else might be wrong with her.

I was really tired after the delivery, and back on the ward I slept. When I woke up it was night, and everyone else was asleep. I called the nurse, and told her I wanted to see my baby. She said it wasn't possible, but I insisted. I thought maybe I'd dreamt it, that there wasn't anything wrong, but I had to know, one way or the other. Eventually she agreed to get Simone, and we unwrapped her shawl together. I saw everything then – Simone has elbow-length arms, with three fingers on each, and part of her femur missing on both legs. I just cried and cried and cried. But I prayed too: I said to God, if she's going to suffer, take her now. Because I wanted her, but not if she was going to have an awful life.

My husband was in a terrible state when he discovered what was wrong. They called him in to the hospital, but they didn't give him any idea on the phone what it was about – he thought something had happened to me. When he arrived they took him into a sluice room to show Simone to him – they said they didn't want to frighten other people. He was horrified, he said if she's like that on the outside, what's going to be wrong with her inside? But I persuaded him that Simone would be okay, that she was our baby, and that things would work out alright.

A few days later the consultant came to see me and said he'd heard I'd been putting it about that I'd taken thalidomide during my pregnancy. He warned me not to talk about it any more, which annoyed me enormously. In the end I got the drugs I'd taken during my pregnancy analysed, and sure enough the one I'd taken for anxiety had contained thalidomide.

Simone was one of the last thalidomide babies born. In some ways that helped, in that there were lots of parents with affected two and three-year-olds to give support and advice. In other ways it was awful – why hadn't they publicised the *ban on the drug I was taking, to alert me to the dangers of keeping on taking it once I was pregnant?*

Before I left hospital I decided that we'd always treat Simone as a completely normal child. When I took her to baby clinics they'd sometimes say I didn't need to unwrap her if I didn't want to. But I always did — I didn't feel I had anything to apologise for. She was my baby, and I loved her exactly as I would if she hadn't had anything wrong.

ANDRÉE BOKITKO ON THE BIRTH OF SIMONE ON 27 SEPTEMBER 1962 IN HOSPITAL.

"When I was pregnant in 1960 I attended Erna Wright's classes at the NCT HQ in Seymour Street. Erna was a very exciting antenatal teacher: humourous, forceful, and sometimes a bit shocking in her openness about sex and childbirth, because a lot of people were quite prissy at that time. Her classes were very breathing orientated, of course – you learnt the different levels of breathing which you would graduate through as the contractions got stronger. And she suggested choosing a song or poem to keep your mind active and distract you from the contractions.

I learnt a great deal from Erna, and I put it into practice not only with Oriel's birth in 1960 but again when I had Cressida, my fifth child, in 1965. Cressida was born three weeks early after I'd thought my waters were leaking. I phoned my consultant and went in to the hospital to see him. He examined me and said, well, now you're here we might as well start you off. They were much more casual about induction in those days, although I was Rhesus negative and had antibodies, so there was a reason to do it in my case.

After prepping they gave me some tablets called Buccal Pitocin – these you put under your lip and just let them soak into your gums. And lo and behold, I started having contractions. They continued to get stronger through the day, but the staff seemed to think they weren't strong enough and gave me some more tablets.

With the second dose – wham! – I was in the middle of it. Whacking great contractions started up which practically winded me and by 9pm I was using every distraction technique I could think of, from counting the roses on the curtains and tapping on the bedside table with my knuckles, to singing out loud – as quietly as possible – Good King Wenceslaus and God Rest You Merry Gentlemen. I think the staff nurse thought I was some kind of religious maniac!

Because I was a private patient and we'd negotiated it beforehand with the consultant, Richard my husband, was able to remain with me throughout the

labour. He was an enormous help – not only did he help me keep control by singing with me and tapping on my wrist, but he also squashed my suggestion of pethidine when I began to weaken, telling Sister (when I was in the middle of a contraction and wasn't listening in) that it was too late to give me any injection as by the time it had worked I'd be in the second stage.

He had more foresight than I, because before long my back started to 'crack' with that familiar feeling so I sat up and got Richard to rub my back and did my one, two, blow routine. By 10pm the midwife wanted to watch things at my bottom end, so I had to turn on to my side. It was very *difficult, as I still wanted to remain partially sitting up, so I kept one elbow to prop myself up on and used the other arm to slap my rhythmic one-two-one-two on Richard's back as he leaned over the top of me to rub my back. I believe a nurse from another floor came up with a message for Sister and saw us, and she went back and reported there was some kind of circus act going on upstairs.*

The feeling in my back grew stronger and I told the Sister and Staff Nurse that I wanted to push. So I was loaded onto the trolley and wheeled into the labour ward trying to control the last contraction by singing Good King Wenceslaus *as I was pushed down the corridor. I was rolled on to my side on the delivery bed and told to take gas and air and pant. I had the distinct impression that the midwives didn't want me to push the baby out until the doctor had arrived, so after a while I told them I didn't mind whether the doctor was there, I wanted them to deliver it, and I wanted to push so I didn't need the gas and air – and I didn't want to lie on my back. The sister just told me to go on with the gas and air, and my revolutionary spirit died down and I acquiesced like a good patient. I panted for two more contractions and then I heard the doctor's voice so I thought, here goes, and with that contraction I pushed, and the baby's head was born.*

Before the next contraction the doctor told me to lean forward and pull the baby out, as I was doing psychoprophylaxis. I was astonished, but he encouraged me and I felt Cressida's slippery head and shoulders and heaved at her as my uterus contracted again. So, what with a push from behind and a pull from in front, out she popped – an adorable skinny little daughter. Afterwards I felt elated – I just kept saying to everyone 'I'm so happy' over and over and over again.

WENDY HARWOOD ON THE BIRTH OF CRESSIDA ON 24 NOVEMBER 1965
AT A HOSPITAL IN EAST ANGLIA.

CHAPTER 4

*1970*ˢ
Hurrying Things Along

> *Going to antenatal classes was much more common, but it wasn't universally accepted the way it is now. One midwife told me she thought it was maybe best not to know too much, as she put it.*

As birth became hi-tech, women's needs for information grew and magazines like Parents *became more popular.*

From 1970, having a baby at home was officially frowned upon. That year's *Peel Report* was unequivocal: hospital birth was safest, and everything possible should be done to move all deliveries there.

It wasn't that most people doubted that home was, in almost every case, a pleasanter, more relaxed, more comfortable place to be when you were in labour. But the statistics, so everyone thought, spoke for themselves. Fewer than 17 women in every 100,000 were now dying in childbirth – 30 years before, the figure had been more than ten times higher. Over roughly the same period, birth had become four times safer for babies, with the stillbirth rate down to around 12 in 1000. Meanwhile, hospital birth had grown from around 25% to around 87% – ergo, it must be safer. For many doctors, the case for hospital birth was inarguable – their attitude was to spread their hands, shrug their shoulders, and tell you that yes, hospital birth might turn out to be a bit of an ordeal but it was your duty to go there. Your feelings and general comfort weren't the issue: your own and your baby's health were.

Dr Alexander Gunn, writing in *Mother and Baby* in December 1973, summed up the way many doctors saw it:

'In the long run, every woman should have her baby in hospital because this is the only way in which mothers' and babies' lives will continue to be saved in even greater numbers ... This is bound to be a disappointment to many, for there is no doubt that a hospital confinement has discomforts and degrees of personal sacrifice as the price of its security. Lack of privacy, emotional upset, failure to sympathise with the individual, parting from the family, husband and other children and the conformity to rules and regulations are part of this price.'

For the woman in the street in the early 1970s, the writing must have seemed on the wall for home delivery. Although some were still unable to book beds at maternity units due to pressure of space, the National Health Service was clearly committed to a future in which hospital would be the only place to have a baby.

Not everyone, though, was convinced – although it would be some years before the real crux of the matter, the safety issue, would be brought into question by Marjorie Tew, a statistician who realised that factors like improvements in sanitation, housing and general health had been overlooked in many of the assumptions about hospital safety. Throughout the 1970s a small but determined band of mothers, midwives and doctors fought to keep home delivery as an option, drawing attention mainly to the emotional advantages of birth in a familiar environment, and to the fact that you were less likely to have medical intervention. In October 1975 two doctors, Martin Edwards and Donald Garrow, set out the pro-home birth arguments at a study day organised by the Epping Forest branch of the NCT. The main points made, as summarised later for the NCT bulletin, were:

- *Too little had been heard about mothers' experiences in child-birth, which was often relegated to a secondary role*
- *The whole debate on place of delivery had looked at safety with little or no attention to what a mother might actually want*
- *At a home delivery midwives probably would not use drugs as a first resort: they were more likely to try to help a woman in labour with encouragement and emotional support first*
- *Having your baby taken away from you straight after birth, as happened in many hospitals, might not cause lasting damage to every mother and baby – but it could to some.*

In July 1976 the Department of Health and Social Security was forced by the Society to Support Home Confinements to clarify that, despite the *Peel Report*, the government did not intend to wholly remove a woman's right to choose home delivery if she so wanted. In a letter to the organisation, the department admitted it was aware that many women were experiencing difficulties in organising a home birth. But, it continued, 'While departmental policy since the *Peel Report* of 1970 has been, and remains, to

> **FREDERICK LEBOYER**
> The doctor who wrote, for the first time, about birth from the baby's point of view. He said birth was a painful ordeal for the child, and believed a baby should be welcomed gently into the world. Through his influence delivery rooms became quieter places with less harsh lighting, and babies were handled more carefully and with respect.

> "*It was a good time to be pregnant for the clothes – those smocks with deep yokes, full sleeves and buttoned cuffs were very fashionable, and really quite comfortable in the last few months.*"

encourage as many women as possible to have their baby in hospital because this is considered to be safer, it has never been our intention that health authorities should refuse a home confinement to a woman who wishes to have one.' Because of 'misunderstandings' over this, the DHSS pledged itself to making its position 'more clearly known'.

But while the option might have been preserved for the few, the path to the maternity ward was clearly signposted for the majority. In 1970, 13% of women in England and Wales still gave birth at home; a decade later, the figure had dropped to just over 1%. Hospital delivery had become far and away the norm – and with admission to hospital came, for more and more women, medical intervention. It wasn't just the interventions that had long been common, and which were still carried out – the 'prepping', the shaving of pubic hair, the enemas, the being made to lie down for delivery to make it easier for the medical team. Now, it was these and more – high-dose pethidine and heavy duty epidurals, foetal monitoring and routine episiotomies, bleeping machines and tape-spewing print-outs. Taken to extremes, it was, for anyone who believed birth could be emotionally fulfilling and life-enhancing, a nightmare, perfectly encapsulated by Sheila Kitzinger in her introduction to Michel Odent's *Birth Reborn*:

'They lie like stranded whales, enormous undulations of flesh, immobilized and trapped on narrow tables under glaring lights … Each of the four women separated from the next by only a curtain. From between her legs a wire projects. It is linked to a machine with a rapidly flashing green eye, and from this a long strip of ticker-tape is steadily but tidily vomited, falling in thickening folds as time wears on. Another wire, recording uterine pressure, connects with the machine, too, and produces its own eruption of jagged lines. "Lie still," the

By the early 70s birth control was being discussed and advertised. This 1971 poster got its message across with a combination of humour and drama.

Would you be more careful if it was you that got pregnant?

Anyone married or single can get advice on contraception from the Family Planning Association. Margaret Pyke House, 27-35 Mortimer Street, London W1 N 8BQ. Tel. 01-636 9135.

women are told. "Any movement will interfere with the print-out of the monitor." But it is not possible for them to move. Each has no sensation at all from above her belly down to her feet. Taped to one shoulder is the epidural catheter through which more anaesthetic can be injected when feeling returns. A nurse passes quietly between one woman and the next, checking the machines. A woman asks if she might have a drink; her mouth is very dry. "I am sorry, nothing by mouth." The nurse frowns critically at something on the print-out, and turns to the next machine.'

The ward Sheila Kitzinger described was in West Germany, but its methods were echoed in Britain. In a series of features in *The Sun* (February 1975) exploring the state of obstetrics, one mother who had been heavily monitored in labour reported that when she had asked how she was getting on with her labour she was told it was nothing to do with her!

The main problem, then as now, was that intervention built on intervention in a vicious circle that quickly became out of control and easily lost sight of the person at its centre. The first intervention was usually drug-induced labour, leading to contractions which often became stronger more quickly than would be usual. Pain was therefore more difficult to cope with, leading to heavy-handed 'relief' in the shape of a hefty syringe-full of pethidine or, towards the end of the decade when they were becoming more widespread, an epidural. Heavy drug use meant there was a greater need for the baby to be closely monitored, so from the outset the woman in labour was denied the opportunity to walk around, and was virtually tied to a bed. Being unable to move slowed labour down, and lying on the back or side made it harder to push the baby out, so creating the need for an episiotomy and/or forceps. No surprise, then, that between 1970 and 1977, the instrumental delivery rate in England and Wales went up from 8.8 to

> ## WHAT ELSE HAPPENED IN THE 1970s?
>
> ● *Women got equal pay with men*
>
> ● *Britain converted to decimal currency*
>
> ● *Miners' strikes led to blackouts and the three-day week*
>
> ● *Oil started being piped from the North Sea*
>
> ● *There were two General Elections in one year, 1974, and, three years later, the Lib-Lab pact was formed*
>
> ● *Fresh strikes led to the 'Winter of Discontent' in early 1979*
>
> ● *Margaret Thatcher became Britain's first woman Prime Minister.*

More royal babies attracted attention in the 1970s including Princess Anne's son Peter.

"There were some 20 babies in the ward behind that Checkpoint-Charlie of a window, and I shuffled forward in the queue of freshly-minted fathers to take my turn at the window and gaze at the baby held by a nurse wearing a starched apron and perfunctory smile.

The baby stared at me coolly, unimpressed. I tapped tentatively on the glass, like a child in a zoo, not knowing what to expect but hoping for some reaction. The nurse reacted with a frown, glanced at the baby's wrist, then looked at me with puzzlement. "What's your name?" she mouthed though the sealed glass.

"Walsh," I mouthed back, lips enunciating like elastic bands.

The nurse looked startled, peered again at the baby's wrist band, then abruptly disappeared from the window. She returned a moment later, and the baby she now proffered was actually mine. He wasn't wearing flares, but I could see the resemblance: he had hair in places where I had already lost mine."

Colin Walsh, on the birth of his eldest son in 1970

13.4%. In 1974, the high rate of intervention in childbirth prompted the Central Midwives Board to issue a policy statement stressing the need for student midwives to receive instruction in 'natural birth' as well as 'active management of labour' – presumably, some midwives were in danger of completing their entire training without ever being present at a delivery which progressed completely naturally!

But of the many ways in which obstetric intervention in the 1970s overstretched the mark, it was induction that came to represent most clearly what had gone wrong. Induction, a way of starting off labour by drugs or by rupturing the sac of amniotic fluid, had a host of legitimate uses where early delivery became essential. But in the 1970s, the possibility of being able to set labour off at a certain time and in a certain place began to eclipse the reasoning behind why it was being done. Little by little, the excuses for breaking a woman's waters or setting her up with a syntocinon drip became thinner and thinner, so that by the middle of the decade the induction rate was up from the 8.9% of all deliveries it had been a decade before, to an unbelievable 38.9% in 1974. In some hospitals, women were admitted a few days before their estimated delivery date (EDD) so that induction could take place on that day if labour had not started naturally by then, regardless of the fact that babies are more likely to arrive after than before their EDDs, and that postmaturity would not usually be a problem at this stage. As time went on, babies were being induced merely so they put in an appearance between 9am and 5pm, or so they weren't born at a weekend, or so their arrival didn't coincide with an obstetrician's annual leave.

The whole *débâcle* reached a climax in December 1974 when word reached the NCT that several maternity units had decided to close down for Christmas – women expecting babies around that time were being told they would have to go in early for inductions so their babies did not coincide with the holiday season. An incensed Lady Micklethwait, the then president of the NCT, wrote to the *Guardian* and the *Daily Telegraph* lamenting the sad fact that, at a season commemorating the birth of a child, there was to be 'no room at the inn' for these newborns.

Her cry struck an immediate chord. Within days it became clear that it wasn't only the NCT and mothers who were dismayed by the induction rate – Dr William Liston, lecturer in obstetrics at Aberdeen University, was reported in the *Daily Telegraph* as calling the move to close maternity units over Christmas 'crazy, selfish and very wrong'. Induced babies could be born prematurely, in rare cases, they could even die, he said. His fears were echoed by a fellow doctor who suggested that if drugs given to induce were too strong, the baby might suffer brain damage.

For their part, the hospitals argued that it was safer for babies to arrive during daylight hours when they were better staffed and so better equipped to deal with any emergencies that arose. But the excuse seemed unconvincing – surely the answer, retorted many critics, was to improve hospital cover at night-time? Even the Secretary of the Royal College of Obstetricians and Gynaecologists was quoted as saying that a 'biscuit factory mentality' seemed to be developing in some units. Many midwives, too, declared themselves extremely worried by the trend; Lady Micklethwait testified to how many she had come into contact with, and the *Nursing Times* came out in sympathy with her views.

The row led to questions in the House of Commons to Social Services Secretary Barbara Castle. In reply, Mrs Castle said she: 'Would expect the use of induction to be fully discussed and agreed between the woman and her doctor. It would, of course, be quite wrong for the hospital to put pressure on the woman to agree to induction purely for the convenience of the staff.'

Clearly, though, women were not always, or even often, being properly consulted about induction. In a questionnaire in *Mother and Baby* magazine in 1976, only 24% of 1,100 respondents who had had induced deliveries said they felt they had shared in the decision.

For others, though, the pain of an induced delivery left even deeper scars than the feeling of having been excluded. In an article in the *Guardian* on 2 March 1975, mention was made of one woman who had an abortion to avoid a second induced childbirth; of a husband who had a vasectomy solely to ensure that his wife was not put through another induction; and of a pregnant midwife who hid in a hospital lavatory until her labour was well advanced to avoid the risk of being put on a drip.

Early Learning Centres, launched in the early 1970s, offered parents good quality educational toys in a child-friendly environment. An instant hit with dedicated parents, no shopping trip was complete without a browse in this toy store combined with time in the play area.

"I had my baby privately, and there was no question of going overdue. The specialist said if nothing had happened by the next day, I'd be induced – and I was."

Frederick Leboyer was convinced that the emotional environment of birth is deeply significant throughout an individual's life and his book Birth Without Violence spread his message, and led to a gradual revolution in labour rooms up and down the country.

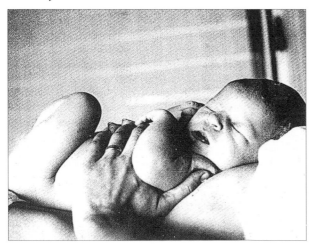

Happily, not all the medical interventions of the 1970s were as dubious as induction. As the decade wore on, there was great excitement about the new machines which could take pictures of the fetus in the uterus, and could be used to date a pregnancy and check on the baby's development. Ultrasound scanning, first used in underwater U-boat detection during the Second World War, had now found itself a healthier role for peacetime. By the end of the decade many maternity units possessed their own scanning equipment, although routine scans were not yet usual. But the implications of the new machines were clearly far-reaching, and would give obstetricians and midwives their first safe (for so it seemed, and largely continues to seem) means of peering in through the walls of the womb at the baby-to-be. From the start, its use was linked to the testing of the fetus for abnormalities, as it made the relatively recent amniocentesis tests, where a needle was inserted into the uterus to draw off some amniotic fluid for analysis, safer by providing a view into where the best place was for the puncture to be made.

The advent of scans and antenatal tests put the baby's condition and health at the forefront of parents' and medical peoples' minds long before it was due to be born. At the same time, interest was growing in the child's emotional wellbeing, especially in the hours straight after birth. In the past, newborns had not been accorded much in the way of respect: typically, they would be swung from their heels straight after delivery, given to their mothers for a brief introduction, and then packed off to a lonely nursery cot from which to emerge only for four-hourly feeds. More recently, midwives in some hospitals were becoming convinced of the advantages of rooming-in, the policy of keeping the baby beside its mother's bed during her stay in hospital. This, it was realised, helped establish breastfeeding and boosted the bonding process.

Then, in 1975, a book was published which was to revolutionise the way parents, midwives and obstetricians would treat babies at the time of birth. Frederick Leboyer's *Birth Without Violence* pointed out that while everyone else usually smiled and laughed right after a baby was born, the child itself tended to cry inconsolably. The reason, said Dr Leboyer, was the way he was handled:

blinded by harsh, naked lights, deafened by a chaos of sound, abandoned in a hostile environment – was there any surprise he screwed up his face and howled?

What modern obstetrics was doing wrong, said Leboyer, was failing to address the question of how birth felt from the child's point of view. Everyone else: mother, father, midwife, doctor, had had his or her role analysed, debated, thought through. But the baby wasn't considered at all. He wasn't even considered to be a real person at all. Being delivered into the world, from his point of view, was an ordeal of unthinkably horrific proportions – 'the torture of an innocent,' said Leboyer. His text was strongly emotive:

'What makes being born so frightful is the intensity, the vastness and variety of the experience; its stifling richness.
People say – and believe – that a newborn baby feels nothing. He feels *everything.*
Everything – utterly, without choice or filter or discrimination.
Birth is a tidal wave of sensation, surpassing anything we can imagine.
A sensory experience so huge we can barely conceive of it.
The baby's senses are at work. Totally.
They have the sharpness and freshness of absolute youth.
What are our senses compared to theirs?
And the sensations of birth are made still more intense by contrast with what life was like before; because the senses were already at work long before the baby was here, among us, in our world.
Admittedly, these sensations are not yet organized into integrated, coherent perceptions. But this makes them all the stronger, all the more violent, unbearable, bewildering.'

Leboyer's book, and the film he made subsequently showing childbirth by his method, was a huge hit. Within months it was a bestseller, and scores of British midwives, obstetricians and mothers-to-be were converted to his views.

In delivery rooms up and down the country, things began to change. Lights were dimmed; voices lowered. Some went the whole Leboyer hog, which included not cutting the cord until it had finished pulsating; massaging the baby straight after birth, preferably on the mother's abdomen; not

TOP 20 *Names of the 1970s*	
BOYS	**G**IRLS
Stephen	Claire
Mark	Sarah
Paul	Nicola
Andrew	Emma
David	Joanne
Richard	Helen
Matthew	Rachel
Daniel	Lisa
Christopher	Rebecca
Darren	Karen

SOURCE: *THE GUINNESS BOOK OF NAMES*, 7TH EDITION

Mrs Susan Bennett with her quads, Emma, Nicola, Claire and Paul, after their birth in July 1974. In the early years of fertility drugs, multiple births of more than three babies became relatively common, but at this time they were still rare. With improvements in the care of low birth-weight babies, the chances of survival improved dramatically.

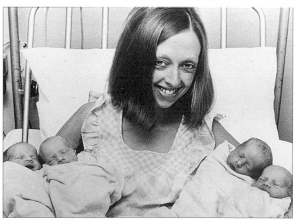

THE BIRTH OF A MIRACLE

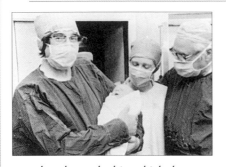

On 25 July 1978, the whole world held its breath as a baby was born. She arrived amidst a storm of controversy, and there were predictions that she'd be grossly deformed, or terribly disabled. But little Louise Brown was healthy and hearty – a completely ordinary baby in every way but the method in which she was conceived. Because, after more than 10 years of research, doctors Patrick Steptoe and Robert Edwards had finally achieved the world's first test-tube baby.

John and Lesley Brown had been trying to have a baby for many years. Eventually, the couple insisted on a proper investigation, which revealed that Lesley had blocked fallopian tubes. Infertility, remembered John, wasn't much discussed at the time. 'You kept it quiet if you couldn't have children and if other people were aware of it they didn't know how to talk to you.'

When Lesley was 29, she was told finally she wouldn't be able to have a child. The couple thought about adoption or fostering – but then, in desperation, they decided to go back to their doctor one last time and were referred to Mr Steptoe.

The Browns contacted Mr Steptoe, and some months later were told there was a chance of taking an egg from Lesley's ovaries, fertilising it with John's sperm, and implanting it back inside Lesley. The couple were ecstatic at the hope, however faint, of a pregnancy. What they didn't realise was that the treatment, though previously tried, had never worked successfully.

It was a year after the Browns met Mr Steptoe, and two operations later, that Lesley had her implant. A pregnancy test a few weeks later confirmed it had been successful, and nine months later Louise made her entrance via a caesarean operation at Oldham General Hospital. The birth was filmed, and the media clamoured for information about the baby who had made history. Desperate for information, some reporters even dressed up as nuns to try to get into the maternity wards – while another sparked off a bomb scare to try to flush the Browns out onto the street. And when Lesley and Louise returned home, the ambulance carrying them couldn't even get into their street for press cars blocking the road.

Eighteen years on, many thousands more babies have been born after In Vitro Fertilisation (IVF). Mr Steptoe, who died in 1988, and Professor Edwards, went on to set up Bourn Hall near Cambridge, a clinic specialising in the treatment of infertile couples.

sucking the baby's breathing tubes out, but draining any mucus by lying him down correctly; and, the Leboyer trademark, bathing the child in warm water soon after the delivery – this was to reassure him by returning him to an environment similar to the one he had just left inside the womb.

Leboyer's ideal delivery, needless to say, was difficult to achieve in the high-tech medical environment that had become so typical of the 1970s. Some of the technologists hit back, especially when it became clear how influential he had become. It was all very well for Leboyer to wax lyrical about perfect deliveries, they said, but sometimes monitoring or intervention, which inevitably caused noise and bright lights, could save a baby's life. And many poured cold water on his bath idea: if the water wasn't exactly the right temperature, they said, there could be serious risks for the child.

More surprisingly, Leboyer also found himself at odds with the teachers of psychoprophylaxis, because he argued that blocking the sensations of labour was not, truly speaking, natural. He much preferred the approach to labour now being pioneered by NCT teacher, writer and anthropologist, Sheila Kitzinger, who had built on the work of Dick-Read and Lamaze (the originator of psychoprophylaxis) to evolve what became known as the psychosexual method of dealing with labour.

In terms of making women more aware of the issues and politics of childbirth, Kitzinger has been an unparalleled force over the last 20 years in Britain. But back in the 1970s, her most significant contribution was to attach a new possibility to the business of having a baby. Childbirth, she said, could be achieved with joy. Others had said childbirth could be without fear, or without pain, or without intervention. But for Kitzinger, having a baby wasn't just without something. It was a positive experience: not merely an ordeal you 'got through' and thought yourself lucky to emerge from with your baby and life intact, but a potentially crucial, life-changing milestone. Childbirth, like sex and death, was an event that grounded us as human beings, one of the most central, significant and creative opportunities of a woman's life.

Kitzinger introduced another visionary in the field of childbirth, the obstetrician Michel Odent, as a speaker to Britain and North America.

Odent, a French doctor, had been inspired by the ideas of his fellow-countryman Leboyer – but he had combined Leboyer's concern for the baby with a deep interest in the mother's wellbeing, too. In his hospital at Pithiviers outside Paris he pioneered a way of giving birth that, like Kitzinger's approach, followed a woman's own instinct of what felt right in labour.

His unit was virtually devoid of technology, almost drug-free, and midwife-run – everything, in other words, that most maternity units, in France as well as Britain, were not. In *Birth Reborn*, the book in which Odent first explained his ideas, the most striking feature is the photographs in which the obstetrician is shown, shirt sleeves rolled up, supporting women as they stand or squat to deliver their babies. Not for

MICHEL ODENT

The French doctor whose work showed the importance of a supportive environment for a successful delivery. At his clinic outside Paris, women would be invited to labour in homely rooms with baths and the minimum of medical intervention or disruption.

By the mid 1970s NCT antenatal classes, like the one below, were in great demand. The combination of information and discussion offered parents an effective preparation for childbirth.

Dr Hugh Jolly

The London paediatrician, whose *Book of Child Care* was a huge bestseller, took over from Dr Spock as the expert of the decade.

"I had three babies, and each time I had to endure prepping, as they called it. This included an enema. At one delivery I was given an enema even though I was in quite advanced labour, and looking back I'm sure it was totally unnecessary. It was certainly complete agony, I can honestly say it was the worst thing about any of my deliveries. I believe these days they don't bother with prepping at all. It makes me quite angry to remember that we had to suffer it, if it wasn't even useful. It really coloured my memories of the deliveries of my babies."

him the surgeon's mask, the delivery table and the stirrups – Odent and his midwives trusted a woman's basic ability to give birth, and believed that emotional and physical support, but not medical intervention, were the most important ingredients those around her could provide.

But these big ideas, though they would become mould-breaking and have important implications for women giving birth in the 1980s, were not widespread during the 1970s. Ordinary mothers having babies in Britain at that time were far more likely to be excited by the possibility of innovations like the new DIY pregnancy-testing kit, which promised results as soon as two weeks after your missed period, and involved mixing a chemical reagent with a test-tube of urine collected after ten hours without anything to eat or drink.

When you got to having the baby there was now the opportunity, in some areas, to have a Domino (Domiciliary In and Out) delivery, in which a community midwife would attend you at home in labour, accompany you into hospital, oversee the delivery and return home with you and your baby to settle you back in. Even where Domino wasn't yet available, an increasing number of areas were offering a 'planned early discharge', which gave you the opportunity to go home from hospital as soon as 48 hours after the birth. In some areas women on the scheme returned by ambulance in their nightdresses – leaflets given to them during pregnancy suggested they take an overcoat and 'substantial slippers' for the journey home!

In the media, the passage of the Sex Discrimination Act through parliament had produced a debate on the future of midwifery, one of the few occupations in which it was men, rather than women, who were excluded. Would the Act open the doors to male midwives, or should government ministers intervene to ensure midwifery remained a special case? Was it appropriate, or desirable, to have midwives who were men?

The issue spawned a host of headlines and generated a cloud of hot air, but at the end of the day it seemed a bit of a red herring. Surveys found the majority of women (66% and more) felt they would not mind their baby being delivered by a male midwife, and the reality, when men were eventually admitted to the ranks of midwives in 1974, was that there weren't many takers anyway.

But as fathers men had, by the end of the decade, pretty well established their right to be there for the birth. The only trouble was that being there for the birth itself didn't mean, as far as many midwives were concerned, that they could remain in the delivery room while 'prepping' or examinations were being carried out. They were also required to don full theatre gear for the actual delivery, which meant more time away from their partners' sides at a time when they were often desperately needed.

Indeed, being a dad at a delivery in the 1970s could be a lonely and soul-destroying business, as Peter and Elizabeth Fenwick relayed in *The Baby Book for Fathers*. On arrival at the hospital, they warned, a couple would be split up immediately while the mother-to-be was whisked away 'for the ritual of bath, shave and enema which are still in most hospitals the routine preparations for childbirth'. While this was going on, the authors cautioned, 'you may find yourself out on a limb, abandoned in the entrance hall feeling lonely, unwanted, even slightly tearful. For at this stage there is no place for fathers in the system. With luck someone will remember to tell you where you may sit and wait. If everyone ignores you as of no more than passing interest in this drama, take out the good book you should have brought with you to steady your nerves and give them half an hour or so, by which time your wife should be hygenically packaged in her hospital nightgown and safely installed in the labour ward.'

In his introduction to the Fenwicks' book, obstetrician Peter Huntingford took up the men's cause. Why, he asked, should they be so treated?

> 'Why should he not share responsibility with his partner, and her medical attendants, for her care? Why should he be sent out of the room when treatment is given and examinations made during labour? These symbols of the barriers that are erected to male participation in childbearing mean that there is ... less chance for fathers to share the sensations and emotions of birth.'

GORDON BOURNE

The obstetrician whose book *Pregnancy*, first published in 1972, became the most comprehensive and best-read book on antenatal care of the decade.

Despite all the new innovations, some traditional products remained popular.

"I was 26 weeks pregnant – well over half-way through – when my GP dropped a bombshell. From the size of the fetus, he said, I was only 19 weeks' pregnant. I'd had some bleeding early on, and we decided I must have lost the first baby and immediately conceived another. It was an awful psychological blow: pregnancy was uncomfortable enough without having to endure another two months! A new estimated date was arrived at, quite arbitrarily as it turned out, and I passed that by two weeks. I had been pregnant now for nearly a year and the urge to get it over and done with was overwhelming.

This led me to misinterpret what I now realise were 'practice contractions'. I thought they were the real thing, and went into our local cottage hospital. I was one of the first women there to ask for my husband to stay with me during labour, and I said I didn't want drugs either, so I was treated as something of a freak who might turn out to be a nuisance.

Anyway, when I first went in it was clear nothing was going to happen straightaway so Jack went home. The contractions carried on all night but they didn't hurt much, which I thought was because I was doing my breathing properly. Next morning the GP examined me and said I was only two fingers dilated. He decided to speed things up by doing a cervical sweep, something I'd never heard of. He said it wouldn't hurt and was less drastic than breaking the waters. But it was excruciating: I felt he was tearing me apart inside and I went into an emotional state of shock

whilst trying to appear normal on the outside. I remember trying to make small talk when all I wanted to do was scream.

After that the contractions came at full strength every two minutes until the baby was born, which turned out to be 24 hours later. Jack kept me company, and we comforted ourselves with the thought that such strong contractions must mean the baby would be born soon. I breathed and just about coped. The midwives were very busy and I was taken into the delivery room in the early evening as the nursing shifts changed, without being examined. Once in there a midwife looked at me and found I was still only two fingers dilated. I'm convinced the shock of the cervical sweep somehow meant the uterus had gone haywire and the contractions weren't actually dilating the cervix. But they were extremely painful.

Having endured hours of what was really useless torture, I was devastated at the prospect of having to go through it all again and when they offered me pethidine I accepted. I asked for a little but I assume I got the standard dose. They left me to lie flat on my back on the delivery table for the next 15 hours. It was a nightmare. I think I had three injections of pethidine in the end. It made me hallucinate, but it didn't take the pain away. I couldn't understand what was *happening and I can still remember being obsessed with a figure of a dog which I could see on top of the gas fire in our sitting room at home. I just wanted to get out of this dark tunnel of pain. Jack was wonderful and I don't think to this day that I would have got through the experience with my sanity without his support. The hospital was old, the staff were busy with straightforward deliveries in the other delivery room and I remember him saying that there was a sparrow flying round the delivery room where we were. There were also cockroaches in the wards, but that's another story.*

I started the second stage of labour at about 8.30am the following morning, but was too exhausted and spaced out to do much to help myself. When the baby was born he didn't breathe for what seemed ages but the significance of this was lost on me.

To my anger, there were no signs at all of him being overdue. He could have stayed inside for another few days and come out when we were both 'ready' instead of being battered for hours against an unyielding cervix. The experience must have been almost as distressing for him as it was for me.

I was so traumatised by the experience that I felt the only way to get over it was to have another baby quickly and do things right this time. Luckily everything worked out wonderfully and our second baby, Chris, was born at home 17 months later, with no drugs at all being used during the labour. I had lied about the date of my last period and given myself a fortnight's leeway, just to be on the safe side. And I went to a different GP.

Anne Loader on the birth of Alex on 8 August 1971 at a maternity hospital in North West England.

Antenatal classes with Sheila Kitzinger were something special. She taught in her lovely Cotswold home, in a huge sitting room with lots of arty sofas and bean bags and floor cushions, which created an air of luxury and made you feel pampered. Sheila herself bubbled with enthusiasm and energy, and obviously loved her subject: you couldn't help but be infected with her spirit. At our last class we were pretending to have contractions when one woman began to go into early labour for real. Another woman, whose EDD was supposed to be sooner, sat on the floor next to her and said, 'I'm so jealous'. We all felt like that. We were looking forward to the great adventure.

When I was pregnant for the second time Peter and I went back to Sheila for one refresher lesson on our own. I was on the GP list, which meant one of the local team of midwives would come to attend me at home when labour began and advise me when to go into hospital.

I started having contractions late one night, just as we were about to go to bed. I discussed with Peter whether to call the midwife, and he suggested rather than losing an entire night's sleep we should go to bed for an hour to prepare for the ordeal. So I agreed. He fell straight asleep, but for me the contractions were too strong to sleep through, and after a while I got up and went downstairs, thinking I would phone for the midwife myself and let Peter sleep till she came.

I was just about to call her when I remembered that they always ask you how frequently the contractions are coming, so I decided to time them first, but it was more difficult than I expected and took several gos before I'd got the hang of breathing through the contraction and keeping an eye on the clock.

Then I needed to go to the loo – and that took a little while, as I had to keep stopping on the way to breathe. One way or another, the best part of an hour must have passed before I got to the phone. The system was that the hospital took your name and called your midwife and she phoned you back. But there was some mix-up over my number, so there was a long delay before she did ring.

By that time I was in no state for a conversation, and could barely get out more than the odd monosyllable at a time before I would have to stop to breathe. I could hear her saying I should get straight to the hospital, but I knew it was too late for that. 'I think I'm going into second stage', I managed to blurt out, and she calmly replied, 'Put down the phone and I'll be with you as soon as I can'.

The moment I'd put the phone down, I felt the second stage contractions crashing through my body; I tried to call for Peter but no sound came out and I realised I was going to have to deliver this baby on my own on the sofa. It was rather alarming, but since I had no choice there was no point in panicking. I also had the comfort that at one of Sheila's classes we had run through the procedure for emergency delivery if your car broke down on the way to the hospital. Basically there was nothing to do but make sure the baby breathes, keep it warm, and wait for the midwife to come and cut the cord.

At the next contraction I put my hand down and felt the warm swelling of the baby's head, and that was a tremendously powerful moment. Soon I was catching her as she slipped out, and bringing her up onto my tummy. She was giving a few little moans so I knew she was breathing, and we just lay there on the sofa in the dark of night, the two of us together.

After a few minutes I thought she would be getting cold, so I needed to get a clean towel to wrap her in. Dominic, who was nearly two, was asleep upstairs, and I didn't want to wake him, so I thought I would creep out into the hall and call softly to Peter. As I got up from the sofa, still holding the baby, a great puddle of blood and goo plopped onto the rug. Fortunately Peter woke instantly at my call and cried back, 'I'm coming!'

He came downstairs expecting me to say I was ready to go off to the hospital, and found me cradling our new daughter. He just stood at the door looking blank and uncomprehending: he couldn't believe his eyes.

When the midwife's car drew up he went out proudly to greet her and the doctor with, 'Come and see this little girl'. I expected her to be warm and congratulatory, but instead she was cool and business-like; if this was a success for me, it wasn't exactly one for her. But she sorted out the mess, resisted the doctor's suggestion that I be sent to the hospital, and left us all happily tucked up in bed, a new family in our own home.

Margaret Hebblethwaite on the birth of Cordelia
on 17 July 1978 at home in Oxford.

"I went to NCT classes during my pregnancy, and the issues there were very much how to avoid routine induction and routine pethidine. Aiming for a 'natural' birth in those days was very difficult – so many interventions were taken as completely routine. But the wisdom of induction was being questioned, and I managed to get myself booked into a hospital which had quite a relaxed policy on it.

Looking back, I can see how small a role the midwives had at that time. At antenatal clinics they didn't do much more than weigh you and test your urine; they didn't have any real responsibility. You'd never go to a clinic and see only a midwife, as you might nowadays. The other thing I remember is how little privacy there was – you'd be examined in a small cubicle which wasn't at all soundproofed and you could hear everything going on next door.

The system was very pushy about getting you to do what it wanted – the hospital antenatal classes I attended were quite inadequate in many ways; they seemed to be mainly about moulding us subtly into compliant patients. And I remember going to a talk from an anaesthetist who told us how wonderful epidurals were, and the same sentiment was echoed by a physiotherapist, of all people. I was pretty sure I didn't want an epidural, but it was very persuasive stuff.

Even more shocking was the fact that they didn't make it clear to you when they were giving pethidine; the midwife would just come in after you'd had your shave and suppository and say, here's something for the pain. That's exactly what happened to

me; she just arrived with a hypodermic in a kidney dish. It was only because I'd been to NCT classes that I knew what it was. So I said, no thank you. I wasn't being brave; I just genuinely felt I could cope at that stage. But the midwife was really taken aback. She wasn't used to her offer of 'help' being rejected, and she was terribly affronted.

My husband, Chris, was with me for the delivery, and though no one questioned his right to be there, he certainly wasn't made overly welcome. And he couldn't stay with me all the time I was in labour – he was sent out of the room while I was being 'prepped' and for internal examinations and so on. Then there was this farcical situation when I wanted to go to the loo and they didn't want me to get off the bed. They brought me a bedpan, but because the bed was so narrow I couldn't use it there so a student midwife put it on a chair and helped me onto it. But at that moment the other midwife arrived, and when she saw that I was off the bed she was horrified. I remember her exact words, she said: 'Don't you know you should never allow a woman in labour to get off the bed?' Shortly afterwards I was in transition, and I'm sure that getting up to get onto the bedpan was what helped my labour along – I feel I was an early example of the benefits of active delivery!

Chris had to go and get all gowned up for the delivery itself, and I was moved for that to the delivery room which was very bright and had lots of theatre lights. Almost as soon as I got in there the midwife, who was obviously determined that I should have some pain relief, slapped a gas and air mask over my face as I started a contraction. I felt the panic rising in me, not because of the contraction but because of the gas and air. After that I managed to fend her off, and relied on the breathing techniques I'd learned at NCT classes. I was also helped enormously by Chris's presence, especially given the hostile environment.

Episiotomy was absolutely routine for a first baby so I was cut, and then Polly was born into this brilliantly-lit room and of course she started yelling straightaway. She was obviously very upset by the light and the noise, and I was keen to feed her at once but I was wearing one of those hospital gowns that does up down the back so it was impossible, and the midwife said it wasn't necessary when I suggested it. And then, only about half an hour after Polly had been born, it was made very clear to Chris that he should leave and could come back for visiting time which was several hours away. I had to wait to be stitched up by a doctor, but in those days it was a very junior job, and no one thought a lot about how well it was being done or anything. I had awful pain for about three weeks afterwards as a result of bad stitching.

When it was all over I felt this wonderful sense of triumph. I felt that, despite things militating against a natural delivery, I'd managed it. The most important thing, I think, was that I always felt in control, and that was quite rare in the 1970s.

NINA SMITH ON THE BIRTH OF POLLY ON 20 MAY 1977 AT A HOSPITAL IN MANCHESTER.

"It was my first pregnancy, and I really wasn't that clued up about labour and birth. I went to the antenatal classes at the hospital, but they didn't give you a lot of information. More importantly, I just didn't know the right questions to ask. My visits to the clinic didn't give me much confidence, either — I never saw the same person twice, and it all seemed very confusing and daunting.

I was only two or three centimetres dilated by the time we went into hospital. They gave me an enema and shaved me and broke the waters as a routine procedure, and then they offered me an epidural. No one had talked about this during pregnancy, so I hadn't given it any thought at all. But I reckoned if they were suggesting it, it was probably a good thing. So I went ahead.

I don't suppose they were as good at epidurals then as they are these days — anyway, it didn't take as it should have done and I was only numbed on one side, so it didn't make me feel much more comfortable. But because I'd had that I had to be wired up to the fetal monitor. Then my husband and I were left to our own devices in the delivery room; we were completely on our own for hours at a time. Every so often the light on the monitor would start flashing, and my husband would go off calmly to fetch someone — but he told me later that once outside the room, he'd gone into a blind panic and rushed around shouting for help.

When I got to the delivery stage I had to have my feet put up in stirrups as my legs felt like blobs of jelly. Somehow I managed to push the baby out, and they gave him to me to hold for a few minutes. But then they took him away, and they didn't tell me why. My husband, meanwhile, went away to phone our families, and I was left completely on my own in the delivery room. It was terrible. In the end I rang the bell, and a midwife came and snapped at me and said everyone was very busy delivering babies!

Alasdair was born at 7pm, and it was 11.30pm before I got out of the delivery room. On the postnatal ward I was given my own room, which was nice. The system then was that the baby was with you during the day — you had to feed at not less than three-hourly intervals and not more than four. Visitors weren't allowed in during feeding times; it wasn't the done thing to be seen breastfeeding."

LINDA MOWLE ON THE BIRTH OF ALASDAIR
ON 16 MAY 1978 AT A HOSPITAL IN WEST LONDON.

I'd heard of Leboyer, though I didn't know a lot about him. But when I went along to the antenatal clinic I was asked whether I'd be prepared to take part in a trial being carried out there into Leboyer-style deliveries. I said I would, and I've been delighted ever since with the treatment I got.

Despite this being the hi-tech 1970s, women on the Leboyer trial got an intervention-free delivery in a room with lots of special touches. There was Tchaikovsky in the background, and the lighting was dimmed and the atmosphere was very calm; there was no one rushing in and out or anything like that.

I gave birth on the bed, and as soon as Enda was born I was given him to hold. My husband was there too, and sharing that moment was very special. A little while later, after I'd given Enda a breastfeed, we immersed him into a bath of warm water, which he seemed to enjoy.

Enda was a very calm, very good baby, though it's impossible to know, of course, how much is down to the delivery. But I certainly thought it was a good way to have a baby – I went on to have two more, and asked for Leboyer deliveries for them, too.

MARGARET JOYCE ON THE BIRTH OF ENDA
AT A LONDON TEACHING HOSPITAL ON 28 JULY 1977.

CHAPTER 5

*1980*ˢ
Women Speaking Out

Bonding was a big issue when I was pregnant. We talked a lot about those all-important first few moments and hours, and set a lot of store by them – perhaps too much, on reflection.

The British edition of Our Bodies Ourselves, *which was published in 1978. Its message, that it was time for women to take on the responsibility for their own health, was welcomed by women of all ages.*

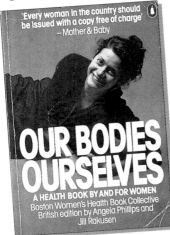

Doctors know best. Until the 1980s, most women wholeheartedly believed that to be the case. Doctors were highly-qualified, professional people. They understood things about our bodies that we didn't, and it was perfectly reasonable if they didn't have time to explain it all to us, their patients. But they had our best interests at heart, and most of the time when they pronounced, we followed their instructions meekly and without protest or complaint.

But something happened at the end of the 1970s that changed all that. Some women, of course (many of them exactly the kind of people who had long been involved with the NCT) were already sceptical about the wisdom of following medical dictates blindly. They felt women should inform themselves much more thoroughly about the business of having a baby, and question those responsible for their medical care about any aspects which concerned them. And from the early 1980s on, this kind of idea became gradually more widespread.

It was due, in part at least, to the publication in Britain of *Our Bodies Ourselves*, a mould-breaking women's health book originally written by a group of American feminists. *Our Bodies Ourselves*, which came out here in 1978, was different from most of what had gone before because it emphasised that a woman's health, and the treatment of any medical conditions that affected her, was her own responsibility. Being ill didn't have to mean surrendering yourself wholly and unquestioningly into the hands of doctors you probably didn't know, possibly didn't like, and maybe ultimately didn't trust. You could ask questions; you could find out the facts; and you could challenge medical assumptions. It was, in the truest sense of the word, a book that *empowered* women and gave them the confidence to ask questions and make decisions for themselves about their health.

Nowhere was the message of *Our Bodies Ourselves* as potent as in the field of childbirth. When a woman is pregnant, after all, she isn't usually ill. Indeed, many pregnant women positively ooze health and energy. In fact, said *Our Bodies Ourselves*, the vast majority of women expecting babies never really needed specialist medical help at all.

> *'Doctors are trained mainly to deal with complications of child-birth. "Well," we say, "you never know. Something might happen. We need our doctor." We are afraid on many levels. We have been taught to have very little confidence in ourselves, in our bodies. In fact at least 90% of our deliveries have no complications. Most of us could very easily give birth with the help of a midwife, in a hospital, a special maternity unit, or at home among family and friends. In actuality the doctor or midwife should have very little part to play in a normal delivery.'*

The authors were not, they emphasised, ungrateful for the obstetric advances that have saved many lives. What they wanted to change was the attitude that said every childbirth should be mechanised and interfered with *just in case* it ran into problems. It wasn't necessary, and it wasn't good enough. It was wonderful that the medical profession could now deal with many of the genuine complications of pregnancy that in the past had claimed many lives. But it wasn't acceptable for the price to be the de-normalisation of every single delivery.

Another book which changed attitudes towards the kind of service women were getting in childbirth was Sheila Kitzinger's *The Good Birth Guide*. This project did something that had never been attempted before: it assessed hospitals in terms of the way they treated women antenatally and at delivery. It was a landmark publication, and it caused a huge outcry in the country's maternity wards – doctors were astonished at the cheek of being given marks for their attitudes and policies by someone who represented ordinary women.

The message of both *Our Bodies Ourselves* and *The Good Birth Guide* was clear: women were no longer prepared to put up with whatever treatment doctors chose to dish out. And just as important as the message was its timing. Because, by the late 1970s and early 1980s the rate of inductions was falling, as a direct result of the campaign waged against the practice by pregnant women and by

PENELOPE LEACH

Psychologist whose easy-to-use, straightforward *Baby and Child* became the definitive parenting manual through the 1980s and 1990s. Her approach is child-centred: her gift is to present the world from the baby's point of view. Underpinning Leach's work is her belief that the first six months of a child's life are crucial to the way a family develops.

organisations like the NCT and the Patients' Association. Some midwives and doctors, of course, joined the women and groups who complained, backing up the argument with medical evidence. But what mattered was that the impetus for change had come, not from within the medical establishment, but from 'patients'. What it proved was that medical practices were not set in stone, and nor were they immune from criticism by ordinary people. And what it showed for childbirth was that the lesson of the market, despite everything hitherto believed, held sway. Consumers could, after all, change the way things were done.

THE 1980s LAYETTE

6 *Stretch suits*

2 *Cardigans*

4 *Vests*

Shawl or blanket

All-in-one snowsuit (for winter babies)

Sun hat (for summer babies)

First size disposable nappies, or a dozen terry nappies plus plastic pants and nappy liners

BASED ON A SUGGESTED LIST IN
HAVING A BABY BY NANCY KOHNER

While the idea was filtering through on a general level, it was also affecting the way women gave birth on an individual basis, through the appearance, from the early 1980s onwards, of birthplans. These documents, conceived originally by the Association of Radical Midwives, were statements of choice written by pregnant women about the way they hoped to be treated in labour. In the early days the plans tended to be quite specific, and honed in – not surprisingly – on the issues of the day. Women wrote often of their desire for Leboyer-inspired touches at their delivery, or they wrote that they did not want to be shaved or given an enema, or that they wanted to avoid an episiotomy if at all possible.

Birthplans have never been entirely without contention, but at this stage they received most flack from obstetricians, who complained of unreasonable women who arrived with 'shopping lists' of demands and refused to listen to any other point of view. Until they became more widespread in the late 1980s, birthplans had the unfortunate effect of labelling a woman as 'difficult' or 'cranky' almost before she'd got her plan out of her pocket.

But whether they tended to assist individual women or succeeded only in building up resentments between her and the medical team caring for her, birthplans did help to rid birth of some of its rather quaint, and by now entirely anachronistic, customs. Shaving the pubic hair, which many women objected to in their birthplan, was one. In *Birthrights*, Sally Inch describes the practice of shaving women before childbirth as 'a time-honoured medical custom begun at the turn of the century'. It had already been shown, in various studies, to be unnecessary and to have no effect in reducing infection rates, but in many hospitals in the early 1980s it remained a routine. Inch suggests midwives seemed keen to continue the practice, but as the decade went on it became harder and harder to defend its use. Gradually shaving was replaced by merely clipping the hair, and eventually it was simply left alone – a huge relief to women who had endured being shaved in previous pregnancies, and who knew how maddeningly itchy and irritating the regrowth could be.

The use of enemas and suppositories to empty the lower bowel during labour was also objected to by many women, and this practice was also – more slowly – phased out. Most women, especially those left to go into labour of their own accord, find they have slight diarrhoea in the days leading up to the delivery, so enemas and suppositories are often quite unnecessary. But worse, they could be extremely uncomfortable – some women have told me their enema was the most uncomfortable part of their entire labour. And as well as almost always being unpleasant, many found it humiliating and distressing.

" There was a lot of publicity in the 1980s about women being awake but unable to communicate during caesareans. It really scared me, I was terrified I might need a section, and when I did I pleaded with the anaesthetist to make sure I was properly asleep. "

Shaves and enemas were part of the process by which hospitals made healthy women having babies into 'patients' – you had to put on a gown, lie on a bed, and subject your body to a medical procedure. Thus, within half an hour or so of your arrival at the hospital, the medical establishment was able to get you where it wanted you (in a bed) and to give you the crucial, from their point of view, message that things you didn't necessarily like were going to be done to you, and it was your place to meekly acquiesce and put up with it.

Doing away with the shave and enema also did away with this immediate need to get into or even onto a bed. (Perhaps it was no coincidence that as these practices were dying off, more and more hospitals were introducing routine foetal monitoring – like the earlier prepping, it got you into bed.) But at the same time, women were beginning to question exactly why birth was something that had to happen in a bed at all. As Mrs W.S. of Hants wrote, in a letter to *Mother and Baby* reprinted in the magazine's book *Questions and Answers on Labour and Birth*, lying on one's back was 'hardly the most dignified, or comfortable position for a

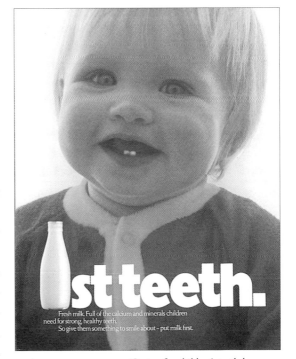

Caring for children's teeth became a national obsession in the 1980s, with campaigns to cut sweet foods and to encourage milk drinking for its calcium content.

This photograph from Michel Odent's Birth Reborn, *published in 1984, sums up his concern that birth should be an intrinsic part of the intimate life of the baby's parents.*

JANET BALASKAS

An NCT antenatal teacher who became interested in the use of yoga in preparation for childbirth, and who pioneered the Active Birth Movement. She inspired the idea that birth didn't have to happen on a bed, but that women could deliver in so-called 'alternative' positions.

pregnant woman to be in'. Was there, she asked Dr Alexander Gunn, the magazine's medical consultant, some 'special reason' why a delivery had to be conducted in this way?

Dr Gunn's reply was interesting, since he began with the completely honest admission that there was 'some truth' in the assumption that 'the position currently adopted for giving birth is enforced on women *more for the convenience of the doctor and the midwife than for the patient*' (author's italics).

He went on to admit there were 'many positions' adopted for giving birth in other parts of the world, though the 'squatting, the lying, and the semi-prone position' were more common in 'underdeveloped and agricultural communities'. But it was 'attention to the emerging baby's head, the clearing of its airway and the whole of its exit from the birth canal' that was the most important aspect of obstetric care – which was why, he said, the lithotomy position (lying on your back with your legs in stirrups) was invariably adopted in Britain.

Not everyone, though, agreed it should be thus. One woman in particular, an independent childbirth educator called Janet Balaskas, who had trained with the NCT, with Sheila Kitzinger as her tutor, was already encouraging womean to get off the delivery table and have what she called an 'active birth'. Although originally meant as a pun on the term 'active management of labour', active birth came to signify a delivery in which the mother remained in control, both mentally and physically, of what was happening to her, and followed her instincts as to which positions felt best during labour and for the birth itself.

Balaskas' first book *New Life* was published in 1979, it was the first book to explain the advantages of upright positions for labour and birth, and to recommend exercises women could do to prepare their bodies for these positions. She met obstetrician, Yehudi Gordon, when she asked him to read her manuscript. He turned out to be an important ally in promoting the principles and practice of active birth.

Soon Gordon was referring patients to the Yoga for Childbirth classes run by Balaskas, and providing a friendly hospital in the Royal Free, where he was based. At the Royal Free, Gordon encouraged women to put into practice Balaskas' teaching – they could move around as they wanted during labour, and give birth in whatever position felt right for them.

But it was a revolution that seemed short-lived when, in 1981, the hospital authorities decided to 'ban' active birth from its delivery wards. The decision was a devastating blow for Balaskas and Gordon, and for those pregnant women who were committed to active birth and had no alternative venue for delivery other than the Royal Free. Balaskas decided protest was the only way forward, and she, with a group of women, organised a demonstration on Hampstead Heath which was attended by around 5,000 people. Speakers included newsreader and mother Anna Ford, obstetrician Michel Odent and childbirth educator Sheila Kitzinger.

The event, which the NCT helped to organise, attracted a lot of publicity, and the Royal Free was persuaded that active birth did, after all, have a future. Just as important was the fact that the protest united women and midwives in a common cause, the first time this had happened on such a scale. Throughout the 1960s and 1970s, midwives had, on the whole, cowed to the doctors' supposed superior knowledge in obstetric matters, but by the end of the 1970s the tide began to turn. A few younger midwives with more radical ideas and, often, feminist leanings, began to meet and exchange ideas – aided, very often, by the NCT whose conferences were often responsible for bringing them together. It was the beginning of a forging of links between midwives with innovative ideas and like-minded women within the NCT, and the influence of this new group within the maternity services has been huge over the years since.

And plenty of others agreed. In 1982, Balaskas organised a conference, attended by 3,000 people, to educate parents and midwives about active birth, the first time a conference on that scale had been organised on childbirth in Britain. Balaskas was so inundated with applications for places that she had to run another similar event the following year. In response to the growing interest in the movement, the Royal College of Midwives put out a statement confirming their members could deliver women in virtually any position.

Active birth, according to Janet Balaskas in her book of the same name, *Active Birth* reduced the need for an episiotomy, which was another major bugbear of the time. So convinced were doctors of the usefulness of cutting the perineum for delivery that episiotomies were now done to almost 100% of first-time British mothers, and in between 30–70% of all deliveries. But serious doubts were being

TOP 20 Names of the 1980s	
BOYS	**G**IRLS
Christopher	Sarah
Matthew	Claire
David	Emma
James	Laura
Daniel	Rebecca
Andrew	Gemma
Steven	Rachel
Michael	Kelly
Mark	Victoria
Paul	Katherine

SOURCE: *THE GUINNESS BOOK OF NAMES*, 7TH EDITION

Wendy Savage, consultant obstetrician, was suspended from clinical work in April 1985 at the London Hospital for allegedly being a 'danger to her patients'. There was a public enquiry, which was estimated to have cost more than £100,000. She was eventually reinstated after a huge wave of support from ordinary parents who applauded her attempts to de-medicalise childbirth.

raised as to their effectiveness and to their long-term effect on women, and leading the case for the prosecution was Sheila Kitzinger, who described the practice as 'a doctor-induced injury'. In her study of episiotomies published by the NCT in 1981, Kitzinger found that women who had them suffered more pain than women who tore naturally, and found intercourse more difficult to cope with. This was particularly interesting given that the medical textbooks claimed episiotomies were done to prevent post-delivery pain, and because they made intercourse more comfortable afterwards.

As episiotomies were fashionable, so too were caesareans. In England and Wales, the number of sections rose from around one in 22 deliveries in 1963 to one in nine in 1985. That year, public attention was focused suddenly and sharply on the rising caesarean rate by the suspension of East London obstetrician Wendy Savage, who was accused of carrying out sections at a stage considered 'too late'. Her low section rate of 6% represented, as far as the NCT was concerned, her sensitivity and confidence in allowing women to labour naturally and only intervening when absolutely necessary. Others, though, took the view that she was not stepping in early enough, which implied she was taking risks.

When, though, was the 'right' time to step in and suggest a caesarean? Over the course of this century, with improvements in anaesthetics, blood transfusions, antibiotics and surgical techniques, the operation had become far safer for the woman, and was now considered by many obstetricians to be less risky, from the baby's point of view, for difficult or hazardous labours. But it was also clear to many that the technology that bedecked even a so-called 'low risk' woman in labour was contributing to the growing section rate – in one report, 25% of obstetricians reckoned continuous fetal monitoring led them to perform more caesareans. The machines would show a blip (not always an accurate one – one study showed they could produce up to a 67% false output), the staff would panic, and the scapel would be out. It was quicker, it was 'safer', it was less nail-biting, and it reduced the risk that the obstetrician would find himself being sued for negligence if the baby was born damaged. From the woman's point of view, on the other hand, it was major surgery, it was painful and debilitating for several weeks, it made the establishment of breastfeeding difficult, and it robbed her of the satisfaction of a vaginal delivery.

Wendy Savage's philosophy was firmly backed by a strong campaign which included the NCT, the Association for Improvements in the Maternity Services, and a whole range of community groups from Tower Hamlets. They joined forces for a march through the East End which included parents with pushchairs, pregnant women, local GPs, midwives, and a minibus carrying Asian women who were fasting at the time. Media coverage of the event meant there was a thorough airing for the whole question of caesarean sections and why so many were being done.

Mrs Savage was eventually re-instated, but the section rate continued to rise and the debate about whys and wherefores has rumbled on. In 1988 an article in the *Sunday Times* said doctors were worried about the resort to caesareans, and quoted one obstetrician who said the main reason for the increase in the figures was 'patience, rather than patients'. He said he had recently delivered a baby at 5.30am following a 12-hour labour. 'It made me a bit tired during the day,' he said. 'Many would have done a caesarean section at 11.30pm, saying "failure to progress".'

In the past many obstetricians had taken the view that once a woman had had one caesarean, any future deliveries would have to be by the same route. But now more mothers found themselves in this position, some started to question the accepted wisdom. In September 1982 an article by Pat Barki in the NCT magazine *New Generation* alerted readers to the existence of a group in America called the VBAC (Vaginal Birth After Caesarean, pronounced vee-bak), and related how a woman in New England had given birth to a fifth baby vaginally after four previous sections. The piece pointed out that the major risk highlighted by obstetricians, the rupture of the scar, was in reality extremely rare, and described the phenomenon of a 'trial of labour', in which a woman was 'allowed' to go into labour normally to see whether things progressed satisfactorily, as being as ridiculous as "trial of orgasm". In essence, if one fails to reach orgasm in an allocated time, which is determined by someone else not directly involved, one cannot have intercourse. Crazy! Yet, exactly the same. Factors such as time limitation can inhibit some people and can cause tension which can affect the progress of labour. It seems self evident that more obstetricians should offer

"Epidurals were quite new when I was pregnant, and everyone was clamouring for one. The big issue was whether they'd be available at the hospital you were going to."

routine VBAC and repeat caesarean only if absolutely necessary.' Gradually, they did – by the early 1990s, a woman who had had a previous section had a 75% chance of going on to deliver vaginally in a subsequent pregnancy.

The overall section rate, though, continued to rise, by the mid-1990s, it was around 15% of all deliveries. The increase was acceptable to many women because during the 1980s epidurals became the common anaesthetic for the operation. This meant a woman could 'be there' for the birth of her child, and gradually surgeons began to admit partners for the delivery, too. Although for many couples it wasn't what they had planned or hoped for, the caesarean under epidural had a lot going for it compared with the operation under general anaesthetic, when many women were too woozy for several hours afterwards to meet their baby properly. Also, because they were unconscious when the baby was actually born, some women found it hard to accept that their child was really 'theirs'.

I worked in the City during my pregnancy, and it certainly wouldn't have gone down well to have mentioned my impending motherhood too often. Those were cut-throat days, and you had to seem tough and hard, not maternal and nurturing.

Epidurals were also on the increase as a form of pain-relief for labour – in the early 1970s they were used in about 4% of deliveries, but by 1988 the figure was up to 17%. Their availability, though, depended to a large extent on where you were having your baby, on what time of day it was, and on whether there was an anaesthetist available. For many women, the epidural seemed to represent a dream come true. According to its sales hype, the anaesthetic injected into the spinal area removed most of the pain of labour, but still enabled you to experience the sensation of pushing your baby into the world. It sounded ideal, and for a time the issue seemed to be extending its accessability, so that it would be available on demand, at any time of day, in every obstetric unit in the country.

Gradually, though, doubts began to set in. There was no question that epidurals were a significant obstetric advance, and for some women they genuinely did work like a dream. But others who had experienced them said they would do anything to avoid another, and some felt they had been bullied into having one in the first place. In 1987, the NCT published the first in-depth report into what women felt about epidurals. Sheila Kitzinger, who wrote the report, found in her research that about one in five British women said they'd never have another, and those whose epidurals had gone wrong were often emotionally scarred by the experience. Kitzinger found that what mattered when it came to epidurals was a woman's sense of control. Where women felt they had been involved in deciding whether to go for an epidural, and where they were given information about their choice, the result was generally satisfaction – even when the birth was long and difficult. But where the decision seemed to be taken out of their hands, women felt unhappy with their epidurals, even when they had been given total pain-relief. One said she felt 'helpless, treated like a side of meat, moved, examined and catheterised without consultation as though my labour now belonged to the doctors'.

Epidurals, Kitzinger concluded, had a vital part to play in obstetrics. But there was a need to 'explore ways in which a woman's decision to accept or decline an offer of an epidural or, for that matter, any other form of pain-relief can be made as one expression of her autonomy in childbirth, rather than as a consequence of powerlessness and despair'. The NCT recommended a three-point plan for maternity units. Firstly, they said, epidurals should never be administered routinely. Secondly, both parents and staff should be aware that their use would often lead to other forms of obstetric intervention, including fetal monitoring and forceps. And thirdly, epidurals could never replace the emotional and practical support of a midwife.

Epidurals weren't the only thing happening at the hi-tech end of obstetrics during the 1980s. Ultrasound scans, introduced in many maternity units during the previous decade, were by now becoming commonplace – and with their increased use came greater realisation of their potential. At King's College Hospital in London, Kypros Nicolaides was pioneering in-the-womb surgery for babies shown by scans to have problems. 'New developments in medical technology are allowing operations to be carried out while the baby is still in the womb,' declared *Parents* magazine in March 1989. 'Babies at risk, particularly those with collections of fluid on their brain, kidneys or lungs, have become patients in their own right, long before they are born.' Usually, the

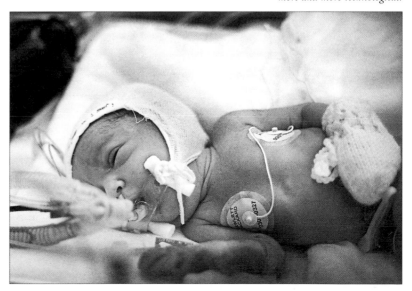

By the mid 1980s rates of survival for very small, premature babies improved dramatically. New treatments to help a premature baby's lungs work allowed smaller, and earlier, babies to survive, and Special Care Baby Units became more and more technological.

technique involved inserting tiny shunts or drains into an area of the baby's body where fluid was building up, in order to drain it and avoid damage to the developing organs. It was, pointed out *Parents*, an important step forward. Until now, babies had relied exclusively on their mothers for their welfare – now, there was the chance of outside help if fetal development seemed to be going awry.

Big steps forward were also coming thick and fast in the field of care of premature babies. Between 1966 and 1982 the chances of survival in a baby born weighing 1000g (2lb 3oz) rose from 15% to 40%; for those born at 1001–1500g (3lb 4oz) the rates went up from 51% to 83%. Barbara Glover and Christine Hodson, authors of *You and Your Premature Baby*, said even the two years before their book's publication had increased significantly a baby's chances of survival. Among the most important advances of the decade were the use of artificial surfactants to help mature the premature baby's lungs; better and more efficient life support systems; and the realisation that the mother's presence, as well as that of the rest of the family, were often vital in even a tiny baby's wellbeing. The concept of a Special Care Baby Unit, which had started out in the 1950s as a separate nursery run basically on TLC (Tender Loving Care) and prayer, had by now grown into a highly-staffed, highly-specialised area of the district hospital where sick and very premature babies would be closely monitored and given round-the-clock nursing care.

But as technology marched on, the natural childbirth movement also gathered momentum. In March 1985, 15 years after the *Peel Report* had announced its intention of moving all births to hospital, the front cover of *Mother and Baby* magazine was daring to ask: 'Why shouldn't you be at home?' Home birth, it said, was 'safer even than hospital birth in the right circumstances – and that's official'.

A survey of 8,856 home births in England and Wales in 1979, it reported, had shown that the perinatal mortality rate (the number of babies stillborn or who die within a week of birth) was just 4.1 per 1,000, compared with an overall rate of 16.9 per 1,000. And as well as

The Mothercare catalogue for spring and summer 1983 featured clothes for mothers-to-be who demanded comfort and freedom of movement.

A	T-Shirt with mesh yoke insert. 100% Cotton	1087-61 White	Bust Sizes 85 to 105 cm	£5·75
B	Jumpsuit with elasticated back and roll-up cuffs. Adjustable straps and half belt. 100% Cotton	1325-21 Blue/ White Stripe		£10·95
C	Striped Dungaree with high back, adjustable waist and straps. Three pockets. 100% Cotton	1329-51 Red/ White	Hip Sizes 86 to 110 cm	£12·95
D	Dungaree with two pockets, adjustable side fastening and straps. 55% Polyester/45% Cotton	1327-23 Blue		£12·95

Playsuit—for details please see page 101

being safer, home birth also gave you continuity of care, more personal attention, an informal atmosphere for the delivery, less intervention, and more involvement for the rest of the family. If you wanted a home delivery you should go for it, urged *Mother and Baby* – though you might need to be 'pretty determined' to get one.

By the late 1980s home deliveries were at an all-time low – some were even predicting they might cease to be an option at all. One newspaper article went so far as to suggest legislation should be introduced under which women could be prosecuted for giving birth at home! But a small group of childbirth educators and mothers continued to staunchly defend the importance of the right to home birth, and the campaign was given the boost it needed with the International Home Birth Conference in Wembley in October 1987. This conference, organised by Sheila Kitzinger, Janet Balaskas, Beverley Beech of the Association for Improvements in the Maternity Services and independent midwife Melody Weig, attracted 2,000 participants from 17 countries. Information from different areas and cultures was shared, and the commitment to home delivery was re-affirmed. As Sheila Kitzinger said later, the conference wasn't just about recommending home birth to women, it was about the importance of treasuring the experience of home birth as a model for birth generally. If that model had been lost, much of what has happened since to improve childbirth for women would have been impossible.

Meanwhile Active Birth Movement founder Janet Balaskas was busying herself with another revolution – the growth of interest in waterbirth. She had imported the idea from France, where it was practised by women in Michel Odent's hospital at Pithiviers – a documentary film about the unit, made by the BBC in 1982, included a birth in the water pool and captured the public's imagination. An earlier pioneer, whose work had also received a lot of publicity, had been Soviet swimming instructor Igor Tjarkovsky – he had assisted many mothers to give birth in a tank installed in his bathroom in Moscow in the 1960s.

Writing in *New Generation* in June 1988, Balaskas noted that, for many mothers in labour, 'there seems to be

This suggested layette offered items for all the new baby's needs – from hats to nappy pins.

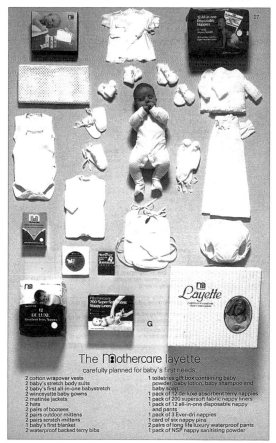

WHAT ELSE HAPPENED IN THE 1980s?

- *Youths rioted in Brixton, Toxteth, and other inner-city areas*

- *Prince Charles and Lady Diana Spencer were married at St Paul's*

- *Britain went to war with Argentina over the Falklands*

- *There was a bitter one-year-long miners' strike*

- *An IRA bomb planted in a Brighton hotel during the Conservative Conference killed four*

- *The Live Aid pop concert raised funds for those starving after famine hit Ethiopia*

- *The Berlin Wall came down.*

Birth and parenthood became the subject of much media attention when Princess Diana and Prince Charles presented their newborn son Prince William to the cameras.

a natural attraction to water in labour. Many women have told me how they enjoyed pain-relief standing in the shower with the warm water running down their back or lying in the bathtub.'

The logical next step, she continued, was for women to labour and even deliver in water. They needed specially-designed tubs, and her husband, Keith Brainin, took up the challenge and designed a portable birth pool that could be carried easily in the back of a car and used either for a home birth or in hospital. By 1988 the Active Birth Centre had two tubs for hire, and about 20 women had used them. Most of them, said Balaskas, had enjoyed the sensation of being in water during contractions but had got out onto dry land for the pushing stage and the actual delivery. But 'a few choose to deliver underwater deliberately to reduce birth trauma for the baby. We strongly recommend that mothers wait and see what seems most appropriate at the time and keep an open mind.'

Waterbirth was greeted by a mixed response, Balaskas reported. Independent midwives had generally welcomed the idea, as had some community midwives. There were 'quite a few' supportive GPs and even one or two obstetricians. But, 'on the other hand we have experienced doctors who think it is downright dangerous and midwives who are very apprehensive about not being able to tell what is happening or are unwilling to get in the water (although this is not usually necessary). Fear of infection is a big anxiety, but we haven't experienced an infection so far and neither has Michel Odent in all his years of waterbirth experience in France.'

Delivering babies in water was a genuinely new contribution to the field of childbirth. But then it was only now, in the late twentieth century, that heating the water to a comfortable blood heat and the atmosphere to the right temperature could be guaranteed. Since these were essential prerequisites, it was only now that waterbirth could really take off in popularity. But some believed, too, that the practice represented a kickback against the high obstetric intervention rate. In water, perhaps, a woman in labour felt she could mark out some privacy for herself, give herself space to move around, and fend off disturbances and distractions.

Significantly, the 1980s saw important links forming between the NCT and other professional organisations in the childbirth field, providing a crucial arena to feed in ordinary women's concerns to the midwives, health visitors and doctors who were dealing with their care. It was former NCT president Eileen Hutton who instigated these links – the first, in the late 1980s, was with the Royal College of Midwives, and led to the setting up of a regular meeting between key people from both organisations. Informal links between midwives and NCT antenatal teachers and others within the Trust, had, of course, existed from the very earliest days, but what was significant about this development was that a formal process was instigated, which will continue on into the decades ahead. A similar forum was established with the Health Visitors Association a few years later.

Janet Balaskas' Active Birth Movement got women off the bed for childbirth and that meant an important psychological shift for health professionals – not in bed meant not so easily labelled as 'patients'.

As links between health professionals and the NCT became stronger, so too did a readiness on the professionals' part to hear an honest appraisal from the Trust on the way midwifery and health visiting worked in action. As Eileen Hutton puts it:

'We had always been asked to talk to these organisations about what we did: but now, they were inviting us to talk to them about what they did. They were asking us for input from ordinary women about how effectively they were doing their jobs.'

"We always knew we wanted children, but after a couple of years of trying without any result I was referred for tests. The result wasn't good – I had blocked Fallopian tubes. But on the plus side the gynaecologist said I still had a chance of conceiving, so we just went on hoping.

I had quite a lot of gynaecological problems over the next few years, including surgery for a fibroid. We were living in Saudi Arabia at the time, and I was quite ill. One day things got very bad, I was in a lot of pain, and I was taken to hospital as an emergency. I had severe pelvic inflammatory disease, and the doctors decided they'd have to remove my Fallopian tubes, all of one ovary and half of the other. If I'd been in Britain, I later discovered, I'd almost certainly have had a hysterectomy, too. But in Saudi preserving a woman's uterus is considered vital, and they managed to save it.

Two years later we returned home to Scotland. We'd considered IVF in the past, but now knew it was our only hope of a baby. After a lot of thought, we decided we'd give it just one try. If it didn't work out, we'd just get on with the rest of our lives. We knew it would be expensive and stressful, but we thought it was worth a chance.

There was an IVF programme in Glasgow but it was in its infancy, and time wasn't on our side – I was 35 by this stage. We decided we'd go to the top man, Patrick Steptoe, at his Bourn Hall Clinic in Cambridgeshire.

At that time you had to be an in-patient at the clinic around the time the eggs were removed and the embryos implanted. I was in for about eight days – I'd already started a course of hormone injections in Glasgow to boost egg production, and these continued at Bourn Hall. I produced five eggs – not bad from half an ovary! – and they were collected under general anaesthetic, as my insides were in a bit of a state after my earlier gynaecological ops. Three embryos fertilized in the petrie dish, and they were implanted two days later. I was discharged from the clinic the following day, and stayed nearby for another ten days or so – Mr Steptoe didn't like his patients to travel far in the few days after the treatment.

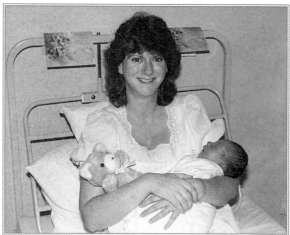

I was back in Glasgow by the time the results of the pregnancy test came through. It was about 7pm in the evening when the call came through. Arthur and I were certain it would be negative – we really didn't hold out much hope at all. In many ways we were quite relaxed about it all – we'd gone through all our grief at being infertile several years before when we were first told about the blocked tubes, and this was just a remote chance. When the doctor said it had worked, we were stunned. I remember telling him I wanted to hug him. It was just amazing.

Because I only had half an ovary I wasn't making enough hormones to support the pregnancy, so I had to have an injection every day for the next four months or so, until the hormones from the placenta took over. It was quite a straightforward pregnancy, but I was very closely monitored, and at seven months I was taken into hospital for bed rest. They were trying to decide whether I should have an elective caesarean when I went into labour, so Andrew was born normally. It was a long labour, and he was monitored throughout and needed forceps in the end. But the moment he was actually born was wonderful – we were all in tears, even the consultant who delivered him. The midwife said later it was the most emotional birth she had ever attended.

We decided not to try IVF again. It wasn't an easy decision, but Andrew would have suffered from all the upheaval of the process and he was too precious for that. He was the baby we thought we'd never have, and we just wanted to enjoy every moment of him and be grateful for what we had. ""

JEAN BEVERLY ON THE BIRTH OF ANDREW ON 11 NOVEMBER 1987
AT A HOSPITAL IN GLASGOW.

" *Waterbirth wasn't at all common in Britain when I got pregnant with Grace, and there were no pool tub hire firms or anything like that. But I read* Water Babies, *the book about the Russian babies born in water, and it had a big effect. I've always enjoyed swimming, and I found being in water was the most comfortable place to be when I was pregnant. So when I read about giving birth in water I just thought, yes. This is right for me.*

I wasn't daunted by the thought that no one I knew had ever done it, or that the independent midwife I'd hired, Jill, had never done one before. I was really confident about it, and convinced everything would be alright. But we did have to find a tub, of course. I wasn't keen on using a conventional bath because there wouldn't be much room to move about or get into the right position. So we started looking around for an alternative.

We were staying in Brighton, so we decided to try the aquarium there and asked if we could borrow a tank. They were a bit surprised by the idea, but keen to help. Then we went to a building centre to look at some fibreglass fishponds, and I thought they looked a bit naff. The mini skips, on the other hand, seemed perfect. I remember asking the guy there how much they cost, and he said £24. So I said, how much would you charge if it came back without any rubbish. He asked what we were going to do with it, and when I told him he completely freaked out and started scouring the place for Jeremy Beadle or a hidden camera – he was convinced it was a set-up!

Anyway, we went for the skip. By this stage we'd rented a bungalow in Peacehaven and it had a garage which seemed perfect as a birthing room. We put the skip in there and bought some polysterene to insulate it and some plastic sheeting to line it and we draped the sides with eiderdowns and curtains so that, by the end, you couldn't tell it was a skip at all – it looked like a wonderfully luxurious bed. And we found a way of connecting a hose to the radiator pipe so the water would stay hot, although when it came to it the polysterene had insulated it really well.

We got the skip organised by the Sunday, and Grace was born the following Tuesday. I walked around during the early part of my labour, and only got into the tank when nothing else seemed to help. Being in water was heaven – I could sleep between contractions and could move around without any effort. Grace was born after I'd been in the skip for about four hours. It was a fantastic experience, really gentle and so right. "

KAY CHAMBERS ON THE BIRTH OF GRACE ON 30 JUNE 1987
AT HOME IN PEACEHAVEN, BRIGHTON.

"There were no antenatal classes in my area, but I got together with some friends who were also interested in active birth, and we talked about the deliveries we'd like to have and supported one another.

We knew, though, how unlikely it would be that we'd get what we wanted. Women in Northern Ireland at that time just weren't giving birth off the bed, and it seemed a really revolutionary thing to be suggesting. When I told my obstetrician I was keen to squat, he humoured me and said alright, give it a try – but I don't think he really believed it would work out.

I was very determined, though. I'm a midwife myself, and I'd already had one conventional delivery with an episiotomy and so on. I was certain I wanted to avoid all that this time around.

I stayed at home for quite a lot of my labour. When I arrived at the hospital reception I was already quite advanced, and I had a contraction at the desk. They wanted me to get onto a bed, but I just held onto the desk and said it's okay, I'll be fine here. They were really freaked out – they thought I was going to have the baby right there and then.

I asked them to move the bed right out of the way in the delivery room so it was very clear I wasn't going to use it, and I spent most of my time leaning forward on a chair. The consultant said later he was staggered at how much I could move around during the second stage. I tried to squat for the delivery, but found it very uncomfortable and so tried getting onto all fours. Rebecca was born very easily in that position, and I was absolutely elated afterwards. The consultant was converted to active deliveries, and became known for his sympathetic attitude towards them, but not everyone was convinced. Some of the midwives said they thought my birth had been undignified, but they were very impressed, all the same, at how quickly I recovered."

Anna Louise Shepherd on the birth of Rebecca on 7 March 1984
at a maternity hospital in Northern Ireland.

" *I was 21 weeks pregnant, and everything was going well, when I suddenly started having contractions while I was out one night. Vic, my husband, drove me straight to hospital, and they examined me and said it was really bad news. My cervix was fully dilated – a miscarriage was inevitable.*

I was really upset, of course, and was put in a room on my own for the night. Then the next day I had a scan, and they said everything, amazingly, seemed okay again. But my joy was short-lived, because when I got back to my room my waters broke.

At first the doctors said the baby didn't have a chance this early, and they should just get him out as there was a risk of infection. But I begged them not to, and eventually they said I could carry on and see what happened – but that I'd have to get to 27 weeks before the baby would have any chance. And then a few hours later I started having contractions, and it all seemed hopeless.

The labour pains continued on and off for about a week, and then – when I was just short of 23 weeks pregnant – I was taken into the delivery room. I sent Vic away – I didn't want him to see our baby dead or dying. Giving birth was really easy – he only weighed 1lb 4oz. And when he was out, I heard a tiny squeak. I remember leaping up off the bed and shouting, 'He's alive, he's alive.' I suppose I knew he was probably going to die, but at least he had breathed, at least he'd been alive for a while ... at least I'd been a real mum.

They rushed him off to Special Care and said I could see him in an hour, though the doctor said that really he didn't think the baby would last that long. My mum had arrived by this time, and I remember crying with her and her saying to me that I was still young, I could have another baby.

When we went to see him later, he was still holding his own. It seemed remarkable – the staff were astounded at how well he could breathe. He was on and off the ventilator for weeks, but after only two days he had a spell of breathing on his own.

We knew there wasn't much chance we'd ever take him home, so we just took one day at a time and prayed for a miracle. He was so tiny he didn't even look like a real baby – more like a tiny monkey, covered with this dark hair. He was so early his eyes were still fused, like a kitten's – it wasn't until around 26 weeks that first one, then the other, opened and he looked at us for the first time.

I went home after a few days, but I spent all day every day at the unit, talking to Mark and touching his tiny hands and feet. He seemed to be doing really well, but the doctors didn't want to get our hopes up too much.

It wasn't until he was eight weeks old that I got my first cuddle. It was an amazing moment – he was still covered in wires and attached to lots of machines. But it seemed a really important milestone.

There was lots of media interest, of course. The papers called him Rocky, after

Sylvester Stallone, because of all the hurdles he'd have to get over to survive. It was a bit of a strain, having to cope with journalists, but it helped that so many people were behind us, hoping against hope that he'd be okay.

It wasn't until about a week before he came home that someone at the hospital finally said they thought Mark was going to make it. He was the earliest baby ever to survive – it really seemed quite phenomenal, and doctors from all over the world came to see him while he was in hospital. Bringing him home was the best day of my life, though it was the start of two years of worry. For the first month I don't think I even slept, I just spent the whole time looking at him and praying he wouldn't stop breathing. But he never did, and today he's a perfectly healthy and bright eight-year-old. His teachers can hardly believe he's that baby they remember from the newspapers all those years ago.

CATHY THOMASSON ON THE BIRTH OF MARK ON 15 MARCH 1987
IN A WEST LONDON HOSPITAL.

"I'd been trying to get pregnant for a long time, and had been on a fertility drug for about three years. I was beginning to think I was at the end of the road — the next step was IVF, but I didn't want to get started on another thing.

They did say there was a 3% chance I could have a multiple birth because of the drugs, but of course you never think it will happen to you. Then I got pregnant, and at the first scan they said there were two babies, maybe three. Then when I went back a month later, they said there were five. Someone told me later that they say there are two or three to get you used to the idea, so it's not too great a shock.

I'd been delighted to find myself pregnant, of course, but now I didn't think I could really hope for too much. My consultant didn't give me a lot of confidence that I'd be taking any babies home — he warned me I was likely to miscarry, or they could be born very prematurely and die. So my pregnancy was a very worrying time, not at all joyful — I didn't think a lot about having five babies because I didn't think I'd be getting five babies. I didn't want to do antenatal classes or even have my photo taken while I was pregnant in case it all ended badly — I thought I wouldn't want any reminders of it.

I had lots of medical attention, of course, with scans every other week. At 23 weeks I was taken into hospital for bed rest, by now really apprehensive. I used to sleep an awful lot — it was very tiring. They kept telling me that if I could just get to 28 weeks there'd be a good chance of the babies making it. In fact, I got to 30 weeks, and then my body just couldn't cope any more with the heavy demands of the pregnancy and they decided to do a caesarean.

I had an epidural, so I was awake for the births. It was a big event — there was a paediatrician and two nurses per baby, so they had to queue up outside ready to come in as each child was born. As the obstetrician lifted each baby out he told me the sex, but I didn't see any of them straightaway. The birth seemed to go on for a long time — I suppose it just seemed pretty unbelievable, really. I couldn't quite take it all in.

Later one of the Special Care nurses brought in some photos, but it wasn't until that evening, when I went to visit them, that the reality of what had happened began to sink in. I just didn't know where to go first — from thinking I'd never have any children to suddenly having five, and they all needed me, and I didn't know who to go to first. It's been like that ever since, really.

The babies weighed between 2lb and 3lb 4oz, and they were all on and off ventilators at first. They'd been born in Oxford because of the expertise at the hospital there, but within the first week they were all transferred back to our local hospital. First two went, then another two, then the last one. It was very difficult, having some babies in one hospital and others elsewhere.

Everything seemed so overwhelming, and I suppose it was no surprise when, a few days after the birth, my body went into shock and I ended up in an isolation room with lots of drips in.

I went home to my parents' home, because we were about to move to Devon (just to make life even more interesting!). So it was to my parents that the babies first came home – first two, then four, then all five. I didn't have any extra help at first apart from my mother, but it became impossible so I had to employ someone to look after them at night so I could at least get some sleep.

We were plagued by the media, which was an additional thing to worry about. My parents were pleased as punch with their grandchildren and wanted everyone to know, but I was cautious. The babies seemed so small, I didn't want to go shouting it from the rooftops when so much could still go wrong. And the journalists kept asking questions about babies we felt we hardly knew – when you've got so many you can't get to know them as quickly as other mothers get to know one newborn. Eventually, we were taken on by the agent who handled publicity for the Walton sextuplets, and did a feature for Hello! *magazine when they were a few weeks old.*

I can remember before I got pregnant thinking twins might be nice, but to be honest I wouldn't wish quins on my worst enemy. It's just such hard work, especially as I'm now a single parent – you don't know where you'll find the physical or emotional energy at times. But if I had to put the clock back, I'd do the same thing. I wouldn't recommend it, but I've lived with it. And despite all their early problems and the consultant's fears, the children are all healthy and happy.

PAT HISCOCK ON THE BIRTHS OF THOMAS, REBECCA, DANIEL, MATTHEW AND LOUISE AT A TEACHING HOSPITAL IN OXFORD ON 13 JUNE 1989.

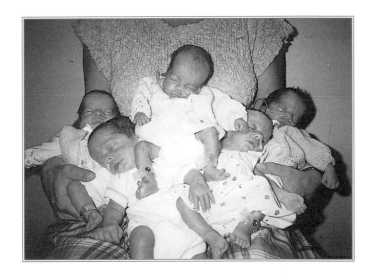

"During my pregnancy I didn't consciously consider that my baby might be born by caesarean. I think I just didn't want to face up to the possibility — and avoiding contemplating it wasn't difficult, since most books on childbirth devoted barely a page to the topic.

The reason for my caesarean was recorded as 'failure to progress during the second stage'. What this meant is that while the first stage of labour (dilation of the cervix) progressed well, the second pushing stage did not. After over two hours of pushing the baby was not showing signs of descending, and I was told I would need a caesarean.

The room suddenly filled with people busy making preparations An internal monitor was attached to the baby's head, a catheter was inserted, I was shaved, answered questions about my medical history and signed consent forms. A drip was put into my hand, and the last thing I remember is an icy cold feeling going into my arm.

I woke up to find Joel in bed with me, and Steve, teary-eyed at my side, saying 'Here's our baby'. 'Is it really our baby?' I kept repeating, though it was more of a statement than a question. 'Isn't he lovely!' Then the anaesthetic wore off and I was taken aback by the pain. Strangely, it had never occurred to me that having a caesarean would be painful.

Steve was exhausted. We had been abruptly separated after the closeness we had shared during labour. Later, he described to me his experience of Joel's birth — crying as he waited outside the operating theatre, feeling scared and totally powerless, his emotions in a turmoil of worry and concern about me, and joy and awe as his newborn son was placed in his arms.

I was transferred to the maternity ward and lay in bed, immobile, a drip in my arm, a catheter in place and a tube draining blood from my scar into a bottle by my bed. It was the antithesis of all my visions of new motherhood. My six-day stay in hospital was a strange mixture of pain, exhaustion (as I got very little sleep) and of euphoria. It was hard to watch the non-caesarean mothers playing with their babies, changing them and handling them with great confidence, while I by contrast could not stand up without assistance, let alone pick up Joel, during those first few days.

After Joel's birth I felt a vague sense of failure, mingled with guilt that maybe I could have done something differently. I also felt sad about the loss of the experience I might have had. I spent a long time trying to piece together what had happened to me during the lost hour, to create an image of how Joel had been born."

SARAH CLEMENT ON THE BIRTH OF JOEL ON 3 JUNE 1987
AT A TEACHING HOSPITAL IN LONDON.

CHAPTER 6

1990ˢ
The Health Service Delivers

The mother of the 1990s is older, and she is wiser. Older because women are choosing to become pregnant later than they used to: the average age of childbirth – 28 – is the highest since 1955, and the number of 40-plus women having babies has doubled over the last decade. And wiser because the range of books, information and advice on all aspects of pregnancy and birth is huge, and growing. No longer is 'Pregnancy' relegated to a dark corner of the health section in the nation's bookshops: these days, helpful tomes on babies are big business, and celebrity authors abound. Over the last couple of years the number of magazines devoted to pregnancy and parenting has blossomed, and more women than ever before are joining organisations like the NCT, the Meet a Mum Association (MAMA) and other parents' self-help groups. Having a baby has become not only something it is okay to talk about, it's become something *everyone* talks about – on the TV news, on radio phone-ins, at dinner parties, in the bus queue. Childbirth, like sex, has finally made it out of the closet as a respectable topic for general conversation.

Along with greater knowledge about what is happening to their bodies has come a stronger determination on the part of pregnant women to be involved in decisions taken about their care. This isn't just an obstetric phenomenon – in all areas of healthcare, patients are informing themselves, finding out about their condition, and asking questions of their doctors and nurses. Pregnant women are, though, in a special category: they have both a huge advantage over other patients, and a huge disadvantage. The advantage is that they are not usually ill, and in fact are often brimming with health, so they have plenty of

"Now seems a good time to be pregnant. There are loads of magazines about it in the newsagents, lots of books in the bookshops, maternity wear in the clothes shops and a general feeling that it's an exciting thing to be having a baby."

In 1991 Benetton's use of a graphic picture of a newly-born baby for advertising their products provoked a national outcry. The advert was eventually withdrawn.

The Empathy Belly is more than just a visual aid to teaching about pregnancy. It attracts a great deal of laughter and the misgivings of some childbirth teachers. The device includes steel weights, a rib constrictor that simulates the effect of an unborn baby on the diaphragm, and a pouch that pushes into the bladder to replicate the pregnant woman's frequent need to pass water. All is disguised by a tasteful smock. Once filled with eight pints of hot water, it gives the wearer – generally male – an authentic experience of what it is like to live through the final stages of pregnancy.

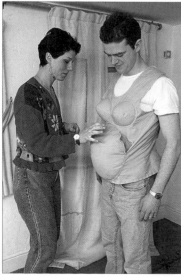

energy to invest in finding out what they need to know and acting on it. Feeling healthy may add to their confidence when they start dealing with antenatal clinic staff, but – and here's the disadvantage – they are clearly very vulnerable to suggestions that their baby might be being put at risk. Every pregnant woman wants a healthy baby – it's as simple as that. Many of us have high – some might even say idealised – hopes for the delivery of our babies, and hope birth will be a life-enhancing experience for all concerned: ourselves, our partner, our child. But at the end of the day, we know the bottom line is safety. So when a doctor plays the safety card, we become putty in his hands. It puts the obstetrician in, to say the least, a powerful position.

Claiming back power, though, has become the pregnancy issue of the 1990s. What women want is information provided by trusted medical staff, and the chance to decide between a number of options. And that's what, increasingly, they're getting, thanks to a series of mould-breaking documents that have become the blueprint for childbirth in Britain in the run-up to the turn of the century.

The best-known, and most radical, of these documents is *Changing Childbirth*, the government's policy document for England published in 1993. Released to loud applause from midwives, childbirth educators and women themselves, *Changing Childbirth* waved the flag of greater and more widespread choice for pregnant women. It also heralded what has become known as 'woman-centred care'. What this means is that the focus of the care has shifted to the woman herself, and her wants and preferences. The 'piece of meat', who had lain so long and silently on the examination table to be prodded and pronounced on by professionals, has a voice at last. And what's more, it's a voice, said *Changing Childbirth*, that should be heard.

Similar, though less far-reaching, policy documents were published for Scotland and Northern Ireland, and for Wales, where a pioneering team were already putting one of *Changing Childbirth*'s major aims, that of continuity of care, into practice. In the Rhondda area, a Know Your Midwife scheme, under which women got to know a small team of midwives and had their babies delivered by one of them, was up and running as early as 1986. At that stage, home birth was down to 0.02%. Eight years later, the figure was up to 5%, the highest in Wales – a clear indication of how much more confident and better-supported pregnant women were feeling.

In England the pioneer of Know Your Midwife schemes was a woman whose name was to be writ large on the history of new childbirth initiatives, Caroline Flint. An NCT antenatal teacher turned midwife, who went on to set up her own independent practice and eventually rose to become President of the Royal College of Midwives, Flint embarked on midwifery with a clear vision of a user-friendly, less bureaucratised, more supportive and sympathetic maternity service. The Know Your Midwife scheme she ran at St George's Hospital in South London between 1983 and 1985 as a randomised control trial of continuity of care involved low-risk women who received antenatal care from just four midwives. This allowed them to build up a relationship with a small number of carers, one of whom would then deliver their baby.

The results of the trial showed that women preferred the sort of care offered by the Know Your Midwife project. Instead of being dealt with by rushed, busy staff whom they had never met before, women in the trial found themselves getting to know a small team of midwives who seemed genuinely interested in them as people, and who became, in many cases, almost friends by delivery day. The trial women reported that they felt able to ask more questions and found it easier to voice anxieties. In labour, they had less analgesia and a lower epidural rate. Their babies were put to the breast more quickly after delivery, and more of the women were still breastfeeding six weeks on. They had cost the NHS less money (shorter hospital stays, fewer epidurals, less doctors' time) and got a better deal. The scheme had proved its worth, and by the beginning of the decade was widely acknowledged as the appropriate kind of care for low-risk pregnant women.

In the St George's Know Your Midwife trial, women without complications would see an obstetrician only twice during their pregnancy. *Changing Childbirth* went further: it suggested that some low-risk women should not need to see an obstetrician at all. Normal antenatal care and straightforward birth would increasingly become the domain of the midwife, and only those who chose to, or who had complications, would see an obstetrician. This would, *Changing Childbirth* argued, give them more time to spend with the women who had more call on their services.

TV presenter Anne Diamond lost a baby through cot death syndrome. Her support of the National Cot Death Appeal in 1992 brought extra media attention and concern for this devastating experience for parents, as well as official advice to put babies to sleep on their back. The 'Back to Sleep' campaign has brought about a considerable drop in the incidence of cot deaths.

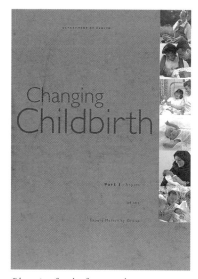

Blueprint for the future – the government document that has ushered in change for mothers-to-be.

Not surprisingly, some obstetricians were outraged. In 20 short years they had gone from being the central figure in every and any pregnancy to being relegated to the sidelines for the majority. The Royal College of Obstetricians and Gynaecologists put its reservations in a strong denunciation of the proposals. 'It is important to realise that pregnancy is a time when underlying diseases may become apparent for the first time in a woman's life,' it said. 'Midwives are not trained to screen for medical problems of this sort; for example, they would not be trained in recognising heart murmurs. We consider the review of every pregnancy by a medically qualified person is essential.'

The document's pro-home birth stance also worried the obstetricians. 'The college's view,' they said, 'is that home confinement is not a safe alternative to delivery in properly equipped surroundings. There is unequivocal evidence that when things go wrong at home, risks to mother and baby are substantially greater than the risks which occur when babies are born in specialist units.'

Changing Childbirth did not, in fact, promote home deliveries as such, but it did state unequivocally the right of a woman to choice. Too often, it said, pregnant women were hurried or talked into agreeing to having their babies in consultant hospital units, without realising there were other options, of which home birth was one. 'Women should receive clear, unbiased advice and be able to choose where they would like their baby to be born,' said the report. 'Their right to make that choice should be respected … '

Where to have the baby, though, was just one of the increasingly diverse number of choices that was surrounding the whole business of birth. One area in particular has become more and more complicated – that of antenatal testing. In the early 1990s the number of tests available to check fetal health mushroomed, leaving many women (and even some professionals) confused and unsure of exactly what was being tested, and what the results actually meant. There were Triple tests and Barts' tests, amnios and CVS, nuchal fold and more. Some tests gave actual yes-or-no answers to the question of whether your baby would have some problem; others provided you with a risk assessment. Some tests were routine; others were according to age or medical history, or by special request.

The technology providing the many tests now available has snow-balled so quickly that it has left the maternity services, women's groups and society at large way behind in their ability to grapple with the practical, emotional and moral issues raised. Counselling should, everyone agrees, be available for pregnant women faced with decisions about whether to have a test, or what to do with the results: but where is the infrastructure to provide it? A widespread information campaign for women of childbearing age to raise awareness of tests and to explain their consequences would be a good idea: but who has the cash to pay for that? And in the general climate of confusion and fuzzy facts, debate about the consequences for the next generation of a system aimed at giving parents the right to choose whether or not to give birth to disabled children is largely going by the board.

In other areas, though, technology is providing advances that seem less morally contentious. In the field of pain-relief in labour the 'mobile' epidural has arrived, and some women are now able to move around while free of labour pain. The new epidural involves a low-dose mix of the drugs given for conventional epidurals and spinal blocks, and its developers boast it can pinpoint the area of pain more specifically, so removing the need to anaesthetise the whole bottom half of the body.

The result sounds to some like a dream come true – a way of being 'in control' and pain-free in labour, able to move in positions that might help the baby's safe passage through the birth canal rather than being tied to a bed. In the most up-to-date mobile epidurals, women are able to control for themselves the frequency of top-ups of anaesthesia once the canula is in place – pain-relief provided by epidurals is often very quick and effective, but it needs regular topping up. But some have voiced criticisms, too: mobile epidurals are still something done 'to' women by medical people, rather than something done by women to help themselves. And the jury still seems to be out on whether mobile epidurals, like the more conventional variety, increase the risk of further intervention and a forceps or ventouse delivery. No research has yet been done into possible long term consequences of 'mobile' epidurals.

"I'm having my baby at home this time around. Hospitals are much better than they used to be, but you're still part of the system — and the bed still dominates the delivery room, and you know your labour is being 'timed' discreetly by someone in the background."

1990s parents expect to continue their lifestyle after the baby arrives and this Jogging Buggy reflects the 'have baby will travel' ethos.

Meanwhile the most invasive form of birth of all, caesarean section, is still on the increase in Britain. More than one in eight babies is now born this way – twice the number of 15 years ago. And most worrying of all is that the rate could climb still higher, as it has in the United States where one in four babies arrives by section. There, fear of litigation drives many surgeons to the 'safety' of an operation rather than allowing nature to take its course. If the baby is born damaged after a vaginal delivery, they argue, the doctor is more vunerable to legal action than if he had taken immediate action at the very first sign of difficulty and done a section.

Sadly, caesareans done partly because of fears of litigation are likely to go on increasing here – the number of families going to court with negligence claims trebled during the late 1980s to 200 a year, and the extension of legal aid to infants in 1990 has encouraged the trend still further. Another interesting phenomenon is that more women than ever are electing to have caesareans, especially those who have experienced a difficult first labour culminating in an emergency section, and who are determined second time around to retain some control over events. The only way they can be sure of the outcome, they decide, is to choose a caesarean, thereby giving themselves time to prepare mentally for what is ahead, and ruling out the possibility of another major disappointment.

Choosing a section also means, for most women, ensuring that they will be awake for their baby's birth, as elective caesareans are almost always done using epidural anaesthetic.

It's easy to sympathise with women who find themselves in this situation. But are those who would really like to try for a vaginal delivery being given enough support? Not always, say some critics of the current system – mothers in some hospitals are given a negative impression of their chances of achieving a vaginal birth, which leads them to decide it's not worth the risk. Yet

TOP: More than one in eight babies are born by caesarean section.

BOTTOM: Every pregnant woman in Britain is now offered at least one antenatal scan, and most take it up.

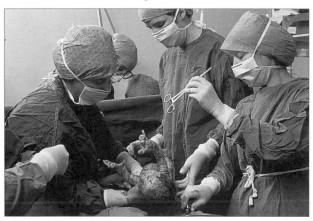

Interestingly the role of partners, which like waterbirths seemed to have been established, has also come in for some rethinking over the last couple of years. By the end of the 1980s around 90% of partners were there for the birth of their babies, but after years of battling to get the trend accepted, questions suddenly started being asked. What, said some psychologists, were men really doing at a baby's delivery? Did they know themselves whose needs they were hoping to meet? Were they helping their women, or were they inadvertently siding with the medical team and helping make the mother more compliable to obstetric intervention? What's more, was it actually good for men to be at a birth? One study showed that 3 in 10 fathers were scared by watching their child's birth, while 3% were actually sick after it.

There was also the issue of whether men were going of their own free will and because their women wanted them there, or whether they felt pressurised by society into 'doing the right thing'. 'In our haste to abandon the old tyranny, which shut fathers out of childbirth, are we creating a new orthodoxy, whereby squeamish men are dragooned into the delivery room by pressure to 'fly the flag' of wives, midwives and other men?' asked Nicola Tyrer in an article in the *Daily Telegraph* in November 1993. The marriage guidance organisation Relate, she continued, even believed it put some men off sex, and led to resentment of the newborn. And Michel Odent, in his 1993 book *The Nature of Birth and Breastfeeding*, claims women often do best with complete privacy during labour. He appears to have most respect for men who decide to wait outside the delivery room, 'Seeming to protect the privacy of their wife from outside'. This, he suggests, is men's oldest, and perhaps most suitable, role in childbirth.

The doubts raised about men being there at births are, though, more than just a backlash. In part they have come about because there has been a more thorough investigation in recent years of the role of the birth partner, as opposed to the father, at the delivery. What kind of support do women need during labour, and who is best qualified to provide it? Studies have shown conclusively that women manage best during childbirth when they have continuous support – there will never be a return to the labour wards of the 1950s where women were left alone for hours at a time. But,

> ## WHAT ELSE HAPPENED IN THE 1990s?
>
> - Margaret Thatcher was ousted as Prime Minister after 11 years
>
> - The Prince and Princess of Wales separated
>
> - Nelson Mandela was freed from a South African prison and went on to become his country's President
>
> - Saddam Hussein invaded Kuwait, sparking the Gulf War
>
> - Bosnia was wracked by war
>
> - The three surviving Beatles reunited to re-record some of their hits

"I was very worried about what I ate. Everyone seemed to know soft cheeses were dangerous – the owner of our local deli was so concerned he used to ask women whether they were pregnant before selling them his brie!"

TOP 20 Names of the 1990s	
BOYS	**G**IRLS
Daniel	Rebecca
Thomas	Amy
Matthew	Sophie
Joshua	Charlotte
Adam	Laura
Luke	Lauren
Michael	Jessica
Christopher	Hannah
Ryan	Jade
Jack	Emma

SOURCE: *THE GUINNESS BOOK OF NAMES*, 7TH EDITION

"I'm pregnant with my third and I'm much more worried about whether this baby will be okay than I was with my other two. It's partly that I'm older, of course, but there just seems to be a lot more publicity these days about babies with abnormalities."

people ask, is a husband or boyfriend the best person to give emotional and physical support over maybe many hours, and in perhaps difficult circumstances? Do they have the stamina and information to give what is required? And are their own needs, as fathers, being overlooked – perhaps men in the delivery room need support, too.

From this debate has emerged a wider understanding of the role of a birth partner, and maternity units are slowly beginning to allow more than one supporter into their delivery rooms. Some women choose to ask a friend, sister or even their own mother to be with them in labour, while others pay for semi-professional help from a 'doula', a trained childbirth companion. Some mothers want their older children to witness the arrival of a new brother or sister, and this is also accepted in some hospitals. Not everyone, though, is in favour of labour parties – at the Royal College of Midwives Annual Conference in 1994 there were complaints that 'childbirth is being turned into a spectator sport as hordes of relatives and friends of mothers-to-be besiege maternity wards' (*Daily Telegraph*, 22 July 1994). As Liverpool midwife Lorna Muirhead lightheartedly told the conference: 'I can't get to the mother because she not only brings her dad and her fella, but her fella's mate as well.' She said there were Chinese banquets in delivery ward corridors and people arriving on bicycles in the middle of the night. 'People could bring along their red scarves and sing "You'll never push alone",' she joked.

Having another supporter or supporters to help a woman cope with her labour means the father of the baby is free to decide whether or not he genuinely wants to be there, rather than feeling he has to go along for his partner's sake. It also means that, if he does choose to be present, he has someone else with whom to share the burden of caring for the mother-to-be – labours can be lengthy, and sometimes even the most dedicated partner needs to take a stroll, get some fresh air, or use the bathroom.

Whether or not a father chooses to be at the actual birth, he certainly has a more active role as a 1990s dad than his father did in the 1950s and 1960s. Or at least, that's the theory – in practice, many new mothers complain that their spouse's enthusiasm for nappy changes and babysitting wanes mysteriously after about two weeks. But even the fact that he's taken time off work to be at home and doing the odd nappy change puts him way ahead of his 1950s counterparts. And there's no doubt that being involved from the start, and being able to hold and touch and wonder at his newborn infant, has an important role to play in bonding father and child.

The 1990s have brought, too, much greater recognition of the importance of continuing support for both parents, though especially the mother, in the weeks and months after childbirth. Where once it was just the birth, and later the birth and the months leading up to it, that were seen as a time when a woman needed extra attention, support and information, it is now understood that the help should continue well into the postnatal period. Sheila Kitzinger's *The Year After Childbirth* neatly encapsulates the trend: unlike most books for new mothers, this one did not focus on the baby. It focused on the *mother*, looking at the huge emotional, physical and relationship changes that beset a woman with a new baby in what Kitzinger aptly describes as 'the roller-coaster year'.

From antenatal care through delivery itself to the postnatal period, the 1990s have seen a number of genuine attempts to care more holistically and sensitively for women having babies. If you're lucky enough to be in the right place at the right time, there's little doubt that this is the decade that has delivered most in enabling you to get the birth you want in the way you want, with the people you choose around you. But some of the most exciting innovations still have to filter through to many parts of the country, and the medical establishment isn't renowned for being quick to change. It may be a long time before all women, in all parts of Britain, are given the sensitive care and support that can transform the experience of giving birth from something to be endured into one of the most fulfilling events of a lifetime.

The 1990s have brought great improvements in the treatment of premature babies, which have meant tiny babies have a much better chance of survival than 40 years ago. But success hasn't come without strings, and many of the smallest babies who survive are handicapped in some way, prompting debate on whether all babies should be saved.

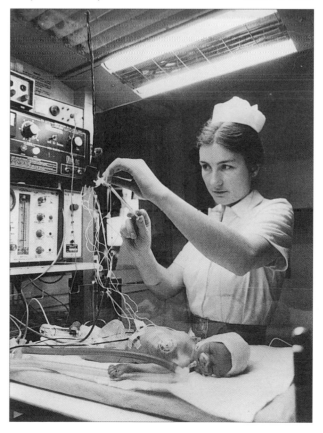

" *My first two babies were born by caesarean, so when I got pregnant again everyone just assumed I'd have another section. But since the birth of my second child I'd done a lot of reading, and realised it might be possible to have a vaginal delivery. I felt that if there was any way of doing that it would be preferable I really wanted to experience a normal birth, and although I accepted that both my previous sections had been necessary at the time, I didn't want another if there was an alternative. When I told all this to my consultant, though, he turned really nasty. He told me bluntly that both my baby and I would die if I even tried it, and then very rudely got up and walked out, saying he only gave patients five minutes of his valuable time.*

I left the hospital in tears, but I wasn't giving up. Instead I went to my GP and told her that I was going to have my baby at home, and how did I arrange it? She thought a home birth was 'a bit rash', but asked whether I'd go to see another consultant who was more likely to understand why I felt the way I did, and would probably allow me what they call a 'trial of labour'.

I said I'd see this one consultant, and that's how I found myself with an appointment with Professor Wendy Savage at a hospital in London. It's 82 miles from my home, but I was prepared to make the long journey if it meant someone would actually listen to my reasons for wanting to avoid unnecessary major abdominal surgery.

I went to the appointment prepared to argue my case, but it was unnecessary. Mrs Savage said she had read my notes and could see no reason why I couldn't have a trial of labour! I was on cloud nine!

As my medical notes said my second caesarean was for fetal distress due to my pelvic size, Mrs Savage did an internal examination to assess my pelvis. Her immediate comment was that a bus could be driven through it — not the most glamorous of comments, but it lifted a huge weight from my shoulders to know that physically my body was designed to have babies normally.

As it turned out, I had a textbook delivery. I was up and about for the first seven and a half hours, and then had an epidural. It took me a long time to push Mathew out, and I ended up with an episiotomy, but the moment when he arrived was amazing. I remember lying there and thinking, 'I've done it! I've proved it's possible.' In fact I don't think I was the very first woman in Britain to manage a vaginal delivery after two caesareans — there had been one or two others — but it certainly wasn't very common. "

LINDA HOWES ON THE BIRTH OF MATHEW ON *9 JUNE* 1990
AT AN EAST LONDON HOSPITAL.

"I was 27 years old, and my pregnancy had been completely straightforward. I didn't have any special plans for the delivery; I think I just assumed that as the pregnancy had gone so well, the birth would too.

And it did, more or less, although Harry's heart rate dipped and I had to have a fetal blood sample taken which was a truly awful experience which involved having my legs up in stirrups so they could get blood from the baby's head, and then doing it all again as they have to repeat the test 30 minutes later. The result showed the baby's oxygen rate was okay, so I carried on for a while. But when I started to push his head wasn't coming down straight, so I ended up with an episiotomy and a ventouse.

I remember that as Harry was born the room went really quiet, because he didn't cry straightaway. In fact he was rather grey, and they had to give him oxygen. But he perked up a bit and they handed him to me, and I remember seeing his sleepy little face and thinking, thank goodness, it's over and everything's fine.

Looking back, I think the midwives and doctors in the delivery suite knew straight away that Harry had Down's syndrome, but no one said anything at that stage. I remember the midwife saying she was going to check whether I was still going to the same ward, and I thought to myself that's a bit odd, I wonder why they would move me. And then they put me into a room by myself, and I remember feeling quite pleased about that.

Harry didn't feed at all easily that first night – he just seemed to want to sleep. Next morning the consultant paediatrician came in to see us, and she said she wanted to take some blood for a chromosome test. I said why, do you think there's anything wrong? And she said no, but inside me I knew from that moment that Harry had Down's.

It was a couple of days later that she came back to tell us. I remember knowing as she came into the room what she was going to say. I was shaking and crying, and I looked down into Harry's face and saw it was wet where my tears had fallen onto it. I just couldn't believe something like this could happen to us; it seemed so unfair. I've had friends who drank and smoked their way through their pregnancies and they've had perfect, healthy babies. And we'd done everything right, not taken any chances, and it happened to us. I still find Harry's birthdays really difficult because it brings it all back, and I always feel sad three days later because that's the anniversary of the day they told us about the Down's."

JOANNE WALL ON THE BIRTH OF HARRY
ON 3 JUNE 1992 AT A LOCAL HOSPITAL.

" *Around 80% of first time mothers at my local hospital have an epidural, so although I said on my birthplan I'd rather not have one, I knew it was a possibility. I knew mobile epidurals, which allow you to move around a bit, were the kind they'd give there, and I definitely felt better about that idea than the old sort of epidural which basically tied you to the bed.*

I started in labour at around 6pm, and used a TENS machine to help cope with the pain — it was excellent. I took it in with me when I went into hospital, at around 3am. Once I was settled into a birthing room I tried lots of different positions to deal with the pain. But things went very slowly. Eighteen hours after the start of labour, I was still only 6cm dilated.

It was at this point that the midwife mentioned the possibility of an epidural. She just said it was another option — there wasn't any pressure at all, and she even left the room to give us a chance to talk it over. We decided to go for it; I suppose I was a bit disheartened by that stage, and although the pain wasn't unbearable the thought of it going on for a lot longer was too much.

Once we'd decided, the anaesthetist arrived very quickly. Setting the epidural up was very easy, and the relief was almost instant. I was completely exhausted by this stage, so the first thing I did was sleep for a while. When I woke up I felt much better — refreshed, and warm in a comforted kind of way. I felt almost back to normal; I could walk around without wobbling at all, and I could move everything I wanted to. I tried walking up and down the corridor for a while, as the midwife thought that might encourage the baby's head to move down the birth canal.

Once you've had an epidural you're checked a lot more, and after a while they said things weren't really moving along. So they suggested an oxytocin drip to speed things up and once I'd had that I was on the bed all the time. I didn't really feel disappointed that I'd ended up with intervention, because I managed for a long time without any pain-relief. Having the epidural meant I could feel in control of the decisions that needed to be taken — I could take my time, and we weren't in a state of panic. Everything was quite calm, and ordered, and I liked that.

After a while the epidural began to wear off and I started pushing. I was so tired by this stage that I needed some help, though, and in the end Henrietta was born with the help of forceps. The cord was round her neck so it all happened in a big hurry, and she was quite blue for ages. I thought my initial feeling would be joy and wonder, but to be absolutely honest I just felt relieved it was all over. "

SARAH BOYLE ON THE BIRTH OF HENRIETTA ON 25 SEPTEMBER 1995
AT A HOSPITAL IN LONDON.

By the age of 36 I'd been working for 22 years, and I'd fought many battles to establish myself in a good job in the City. It was tough and demanding, and I felt I'd put so much into it that I didn't want to jeopardise everything by having a baby. But my feelings changed quite suddenly: I started to think, does power and status really matter? And the truth was, it didn't seem to any more. I'd met a lovely man, and I knew the time was right.

I got pregnant quite easily, but suffered a miscarriage. Thinking back, I know I was working too hard – I think the stress did it. When I got pregnant again, I decided I'd take life more gently. I also wanted to have all the screening tests I could; I knew that having a disabled child would probably destroy my marriage, and I would have had no misgivings about a termination if the tests had been positive. I had the Nuchal Fold test at a teaching hospital in London, where a special scan checks for signs of Down's, and I had an amniocentesis. The results were very optimistic.

My health, though, was a problem. By week 23 I had pre-eclampsia, and my ankles were so swollen I could hardly walk. I also developed pregnancy diabetes, and was seeing either my GP or consultant obstetrician every week. At week 34, the midwife at the antenatal clinic was shocked at how high my blood pressure had become, and sent me straight to hospital. I was in for three weeks, and by then I was desperate to get the whole thing over with. I literally begged for an induction, and they agreed.

They gave me an oxytocin drip, but the labour didn't progress – after 13 hours I was still only 4cm dilated. I'd had enough: I demanded, and got, a caesarean section. Rebecca was three weeks early, but she was fine.

Having so much medical management meant my pregnancy and Rebecca's birth weren't easy, but I don't look back with any sadness or pine for what might have been. I was 39 when I had her, and my age and health meant I needed a lot of medical help. As I see it, I didn't have the choice of a low-intervention pregnancy – the way I did it was the only way I could have a healthy baby.

KAREN LEISERACH ON THE BIRTH OF REBECCA AT A LOCAL HOSPITAL ON 7 JULY 1995.

I always thought I wouldn't want twins, but when they found out I was over the moon. I just couldn't stop laughing. Richard, my husband, was just the same. We were so, so excited.

I'd had bleeding from about 15 weeks, but it didn't seem to affect the babies. It was worrying, of course, but I had regular scans and these were very reassuring. Then, at around 23 weeks, I started to haemorrhage. They took me into hospital and did a scan, and again the babies seemed okay. I'd been really good, having lots of rest and so on, so I thought everything was bound to be alright. We really wanted a daughter as I already had two sons from my previous marriage, and when a scan operator told me at least one of the babies was a girl, I thought my life was complete. God couldn't be so cruel as to make things go wrong now. Everyone else seemed really hopeful, too — a nurse from the Special Care Baby Unit came to tell me about how the babies would be looked after once they were born if they were early, as seemed likely, and I talked to the doctors about options for delivery.

Then about a week later it happened. I'd had tightenings in my abdomen which obviously wasn't a very good sign, but they stopped. Then at about 11.30pm one night I woke up in absolute agony — I've never experienced pain like it. And with each contraction, the blood just gushed out of me.

They put me on a drip and attached a monitor to check the babies' heartbeat, but I think everyone knew by then how things would turn out. You could even hear the twins' hearts slowing down. I remember going into the delivery room — I was almost begging them to give me something to knock me out. The pain was terrible, but I knew what was happening. When I felt the pushing urge I was desperate not to do it. I couldn't bear to push my babies out when I knew it was much too early, that they couldn't possibly survive.

They told me later that the babies were born with their amniotic sacs intact, so although they were so tiny and delicate they weren't bruised or damaged in any way.

The nurses were wonderful — they were crying with me as they cleaned me up afterwards. They told me the babies were really beautiful and described them. I knew I wanted to see them, but I was so scared. The nurse I knew best was fantastic, she was with me all the time. When I felt ready she brought the babies in — they were in a Moses basket, wrapped in blankets. They were absolutely perfect, and quite good weights for their 24 weeks: Alexandra was 1lb 6oz, and Ashley was 1lb 5oz. I remember their tiny fingernails and the tiny hairs on their eyebrows. But they were so, so cold, it was such a shock to touch them.

Later, when Richard was there, they dressed the babies in tiny nappies and babygros and left them with us. We held their hands and talked about them, and cried for the lives they might have had. Again, the staff were so understanding, they didn't intrude on us, but they didn't abandon us either. They managed to keep just the right distance, somehow. Richard stayed at the hospital that night, they gave us a room with a double bed so we could be together. We just needed each other, and everyone seemed to understand that.

After the birth I was introduced to Joan, who was my bereavement midwife; she was a trained bereavement counsellor as well as a midwife. She helped us organise the babies' funeral – we had a short service in the hospital chapel, and the babies were buried in the stillbirth plot of the local cemetery afterwards. The consultant came to the funeral, and several midwives, and that meant a lot. They really cared.

Joan became a very special friend, and we kept in touch afterwards and knew she was there if we needed her. Just over a year later she delivered our third daughter, Jessica, and she's now Jessica's godmother.

KAREN GRUNDY ON THE BIRTHS OF ALEXANDRA AND ASHLEY ON 26 MAY 1990
AT A DISTRICT HOSPITAL IN NORTH YORKSHIRE.

My first baby was born at a large London teaching hospital and it wasn't a pleasant experience. I felt my dignity was undermined, the labour went out of my control, and the postnatal ward was understaffed so I didn't get the help I needed with breastfeeding.

Second time around I just assumed I'd go to the same hospital, until I read an article about the Birth Centre, a new venture set up by independent midwife Caroline Flint. It's a house virtually next door to St George's Hospital in South London, so the full medical back-up is right there if you need it. But the centre itself has genuinely homely birthing rooms that aren't institutionalised or dominated by a bed. I knew straightaway it was what I wanted. It wasn't cheap, but both my husband and I thought it was worth it. After the first baby I'd had bad postnatal depression, which I know was related to my difficult delivery.

When I went into labour Caroline came to visit me at home, and then we all drove over to the Birth Centre. The delivery rooms are just like a sitting-room at home, there's no bed in them, just a comfy sofa that converts to a bed if you want one, and there's a wonderful deep bath in one corner. You also have a TV and a phone and your own loo — and a lock on the inside of the door, so you can shut everyone out if you want to. Not that you need to worry about privacy, the midwives always knocked, and waited for a reply before coming in. The whole place made you feel respected, as well as cosseted.

I actually gave birth kneeling up in the bath. Eliza was a bit white when she was first born, but she turned pink quite quickly. After I got out of the bath and delivered the placenta I sat on the sofa for a while, swathed in towels, cuddling my new daughter. It was the middle of the night, so they made up the bed for me and I had a few hours sleep before going back home at about 8am. Caroline and the other midwife came home with us, and tucked me up in bed, and they came back every day at a pre-arranged time, and spent as long with me as I needed. They were quite wonderful, I felt really nurtured and cared for, which is how it should be when you've just given birth.

Having Eliza was a truly life-enhancing experience, not only for me but also for my husband. He'd found my first delivery very difficult to cope with, too. But the second time around couldn't have been more different.

BARBARA JONES ON THE BIRTH OF ELIZA ON 16 DECEMBER 1994
AT THE BIRTH CENTRE IN TOOTING, SOUTH LONDON.

"When I went along to the hospital I was told about a new scheme for antenatal care, under which I'd get to know and be cared for by just one midwife. I had some reservations, because I'd thought it was just for women who were having a home birth, and I knew I wanted to give birth in hospital. But I was assured there would be no pressure to have a home delivery, so I agreed to take part.

From then on I only went back to the hospital for a scan and to see my consultant. Caroline, my midwife, would come to see me at home for my antenatal checks. It made life very easy – pregnant friends told me lots of nightmare stories about long waits in antenatal clinics, but all I had to do was be home on the day Caroline was due to call. She even carried a mobile phone so she could let me know if she was running late.

Seeing Caroline all the way through and having time to get to know her properly and talk things through really transformed the whole experience of pregnancy and birth. She was a huge support to me when I was having a scan and an amniocentesis, and then when I went into labour she came to check me at home so I didn't need to go into hospital too early. When I did finally go in, Caroline was there waiting for me.

Things didn't go quite to plan during the actual delivery, because Lucy's head got stuck and wouldn't come down. After a while a registrar was called and suggested an epidural and a ventouse. It wasn't at all what I'd wanted, but having Caroline, who I knew and trusted, made it easier to cope with. Later, once we'd gone home, she visited us there and would stay an hour or two if I needed her. She's still a personal friend."

Julia Palfreeman on the birth of Lucy on 18 May 1994 at a hospital in London.

When I became pregnant with my second child in 1993, I decided at about nine weeks to participate in research into the prediction of chromosomal abnormalities by means of fetal 'Nuchal Fold' measurements conducted via ultrasound between the 9th and 11th weeks. I felt so positive and so unconcerned about the risk of an abnormality that I thought if I got the all-clear from the ultrasound screening, I might well skip the stress of amniocentesis.

Having the scan was not a pleasant experience. A young female medical student spent about 45 minutes scanning the fetus using vaginal ultrasound. She kept prodding my abdomen to make the fetus move around into a better position for viewing. I was beginning to get quite irritated and ready to jump off the table when she finally stopped. Other medical people, who weren't introduced, kept entering and leaving the room.

The length of time and the discussion made it evident that the measurement was abnormal, ie that there was some probability that the fetus had a chromosomal abnormality. This was not explained during the screening, although I did see the consultant afterwards and he briefly explained the results. Apparently, the nuchal fold measurement was 'borderline', and definitely above average. I was therefore considered to be in a high-risk category. I later found out that they estimated the risk factors at 1:2, that is, a 50% chance of a chromosomal abnormality.

After the screening the consultant was pretty keen that I get further tests as soon as possible – preferably, CVS. At that point I was pretty disgusted with them, and said thanks, but I will go ahead with my scheduled amniocentesis. The only reason I kept my wits about me was my scientific training. I was upset, but I still kept in mind that the screening is not diagnostic, but just suggested that an increased risk existed.

The six weeks between the ultrasound test and the amniocentesis were terrible. With my first child, as the pregnancy progressed, I began to form a relationship with her. With Thomas I would not let this develop: I kept reminding myself that 'the fetus' was probably abnormal and I would probably have to terminate the pregnancy. I kept wondering what a late termination would be like. My pregnancy became a tentative pregnancy, unsure of itself, waiting for permission to happen.

I underwent my amniocentesis at 15 weeks, and told the technician of the earlier test. She was extremely helpful. She scanned the fetus with extra care and took a number of measurements that can be diagnostic of fetal abnormality such as hand formation and head circumference, and reassured me that all appeared normal. I received my amnio results at 22 weeks, which were normal.

At no stage did anyone ever discuss what would have happened if my tests had found an abnormality. The stark reality is that the solution to such a problem would be late stage abortion. No one mentioned that, asked my feelings about it or described a late abortion.

I only had antenatal testing due to my age, and I am not sure that was even sufficient reason – although perhaps that's easy for me to say, as I now have two healthy children. My experiences have left me feeling angry at a medical profession that oversimplifies, distorts and exaggerates the significance of its findings for a variety of reasons: to gain funds, build prestige, and get published; and is unable to and probably not very interested in communicating information clearly. My experience with it robbed me of developing a relationship with my second child during pregnancy. It was unnecessary. To this day, it saddens me.

JACKIE FISHER ON THE BIRTH OF THOMAS ON 18 OCTOBER 1993
AT A TEACHING HOSPITAL IN LONDON.

"I'd always wanted as natural a birth as possible, and water seemed a perfect place to be in labour. My GP didn't try to put me off. He asked me if I had any preferences about which hospital I went to, and I toured the three local ones and decided to go for the one that had a birthing pool.

There had been a lot of bad publicity about birth in water just before I got pregnant, and some of my friends and family told me I was crazy to be doing it – they thought the baby might die. But the medical people weren't discouraging, though the midwives at the antenatal clinics often warned me not to have expectations that were too high. I was 39 at the time, and they said because of my age I might have high blood pressure and not be able to use the pool.

I was living on my own, so I asked Sylvia, a friend, to be my birth partner. She always seemed very capable and I thought I'd be able to depend on her and trust her. She'd never had a baby herself, but she came along to all the antenatal classes with me.

My labour started during the night, and in the early morning I phoned Sylvia and she came round to drive me to hospital. I was examined and found to be 4cm dilated, which was marvellous as it meant I could go into the birthing pool as soon as they had finished their tests – before I got to this stage they wouldn't let me into the water as it might have slowed the contractions down.

Being in the water was heavenly. I could still feel the pain, but it was easier to cope with – I could hold onto the side of the pool and arch my back during contractions, and Sylvia talked to me and massaged my neck and back. I was pushing for 47 minutes, and then Luke was born quite slowly and calmly, and I remember seeing his big open eyes coming up through the pool as I lifted him out. It was an amazing moment. I stayed in the pool for about five minutes after the birth, but it was hospital policy to deliver the placenta on dry land.

Afterwards, Sylvia said she felt it had been a privilege to be at Luke's birth. And some of the women I knew said they wished they'd had a female friend with them for support, too. I know Luke's father would have been there if I'd wanted him, but I felt it would have been out of curiosity rather than because he wanted to help me through it. The midwife, who had been very keen to include Sylvia in everything, later thanked the two of us because she said it had been a very special delivery. She even joked that we hadn't really needed her, we'd been such a good team!"

Tina Bryant on the birth of Luke on 22 May 1995 at a local hospital.

CHAPTER 7

The Future – Towards Better Birth

How will our grandchildren be born? Will they be coaxed into the world gently, into the arms of their loving parents? Will they arrive via the surgeon's knife, in the operating theatre? Will they be delivered underwater, in a birthing pool?

In many ways, the most significant advance of the last 40 years has been the development of choices for women about how and where they will give birth. Four decades ago, women were 'told' what to do. Today, even when an obstetrician feels strongly about the way he would like a birth to proceed, he knows he must negotiate with the mother concerned. Women know they have options, and obstetricians and midwives increasingly know and acknowledge this too.

It's a trend that will continue – indeed, since the publication of *Changing Childbirth*, the development of choice for pregnant women has been government policy. But, warns childbirth educator Sheila Kitzinger, we shouldn't be tempted to rest on our laurels and feel the battle has been won. Real choice means ensuring women get all the facts before having to make decisions: it means making sure that everyone is very clear about why a test or procedure is being carried out; it means making the parents fully aware of the negative as well as the positive consequences of taking a particular course of action.

So if the battle in the delivery room has been, if not yet won, then at least hard fought, with explanations more forthcoming, where should groups like the NCT now focus their attention? It is another

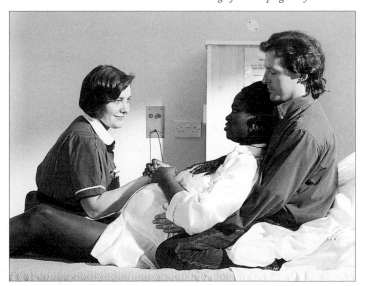

Maternity care in the 1990s is designed to be woman centred, with much emphasis on continuity of carer. Midwives are the key worker for most women having a straightforward pregnancy and birth.

field, that of antenatal screening, which will become the battle-ground in the years ahead. With a large number of antenatal tests already available, and yet more in the pipeline, unborn babies and their mothers are already being routinely screened for various physical and mental fetal defects without adequate explanation of what is being done, let alone the kind of in-depth counselling that is really required.

Until now, screening tests, carried out either via ultrasound scans, or blood tests, have had the broad seal of approval from mothers. They have been seen as a 'good thing', a way of having your mind put at rest that your baby is okay. But the truth is they never have proved anything comprehensive about a baby's health, since they are only ever a partial search for 'markers' that might indicate a problem. Even the more invasive, diagnostic tests – amniocentesis or CVS – can only rule out one or two specific conditions. None of us can guarantee that our unborn child will be entirely healthy, but the quest to achieve that unobtainable goal seems to have taken on a frightening momentum.

The result, as the NCT and other concerned bodies are becoming increasingly aware, is that the level of anxiety among pregnant women is rising, and what should be nine happy months looking forward to motherhood are being eaten away with worry waiting for tests results and scan appointments. Some women, facing the possibility of having a termination if the test results show an abnormality, refuse to allow themselves to acknowledge their pregnancy until the all-clear comes through, sometimes at well over half way through. 'It has an enormous effect on the experience of pregnancy,' says Lesley Page, Professor of Midwifery at Queen Charlotte's Hospital in West London. 'I think the move towards comprehensive screening is an absolutely terrifying one. Where will it stop? Will they start testing unborn babies for intelligence?'

So in spite of governmental moves to provide care of pregnant

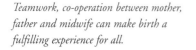

Teamwork, co-operation between mother, father and midwife can make birth a fulfilling experience for all.

women in community health clinics and even their own homes, the ever-increasing dependence on sophisticated antenatal screening means women continue to need to visit hospital for scans and tests.

With this paradoxical situation inevitable what does the future really hold? Birth itself may well move out of the hospital environment in the next decade or two. But where to? Home births have already increased a little as a result of the more relaxed attitude towards it taken by *Changing Childbirth*, but it is unlikely to grow to the proportions of countries like the Netherlands, where around 40% of babies are born at home. It may well move to low-tech birth centres, which will be built alongside hospitals, providing quick and easy transfer to hi-tech obstetric back-up when emergencies arise. The birth centres will be run by midwives – women probably won't even encounter an obstetrician or doctor unless they have problems, and the emphasis will be on informality (no uniforms), friendly support, and a home-from-home atmosphere. Women in labour will be admitted to comfortable rooms with ensuite bathrooms, ensured privacy (no unknown faces wandering in and out as you concentrate on your breathing) and given the dedicated attention of the one midwife who'll have done most of their antenatal care.

That, at least, is the best-case scenario. And the good news is that the blueprints for this kind of more personal, friendly, comfortable service are in place – albeit, mostly, in the private sector. Caroline Flint, President of the Royal College of Midwives, recently established a birth centre in South London run along the lines described above. Currently women using its services have to pay for their care, but similar set-ups are already being considered within the NHS, and there is also the possibility that Health Trusts could set up contracts with independently-run birth centres.

What's more, the way of working which has been trail-blazed by independent midwives, who charge a fee and work outside the NHS, may well provide a model for midwifery generally as we move towards a new century. Caroline Flint is firmly of this opinion: the very fact that she was elected to serve as the midwives' representative reflects, she says, the fact that most of them would like to work as she does, taking on the 'whole package' of antenatal care and delivery for each client she takes on. Getting to know pregnant women well over a number of months, following the progress of their pregnancy, and becoming acquainted with their hopes and wishes is better for midwives as well as mothers-to-be: they get more job satisfaction, mothers get more personal, tailored care.

If midwives are to play a greater role both in and out of the delivery room their status will rise. In the future they're likely to become more widely respected as practitioners in their own right – not just as doctors' assistants, but as *the* specialists in normal childbirth. Knowing where a variation of normal becomes an abnormality is part of their skill, but they're unlikely to move in on the traditional obstetricians' territory as masters of the emergency. On the flip side this means that obstetricians may never deal with normal pregnancies and births which could leave junior obstetricians unrealistically trained. To them a caesarean could become the norm and the safe alternative.

If midwife-run birth centres is the best-case scenario what might be termed the worst-case scenario for the future of childbirth? While all looks set fair for women who sail through their pregnancy and labour, the outlook seems very different for anyone who veers from the path of what the professionals deem to be normal. They can expect to be whisked off to a state-of-the-art, hi-tech hospital birthing unit in which, if strategists are not careful, women could end up feeling even more disempowered and alienated than they did during the technology-mad 1970s.

With more than 15% of births in Britain now via a section, and the figure set to rise still further. Professor James Drife, co-editor of *Contemporary Reviews in Obstetrics and Gynaecology*, believes it will be some time before the number of caesareans begins to level off. As the means of evaluating and testing women in labour become more sophisticated, so the number of potential problems to identify increases more and more sections are being performed 'just in case'.

One of the consequences of this kind of delivery can be emotional turmoil, especially where a section is carried out as an emergency and the decision only made once labour is well advanced. It isn't only

---

THE NCT TODAY

Forty years after its foundation, the National Childbirth Trust continues to work to enable all parents to have an experience of pregnancy, birth and early parenting that enriches their lives and provides a sound foundation for parenthood.

The Trust was founded on a belief that an enriching experience of birth, breastfeeding and parenting is of fundamental importance to every parent and to society, and that continues to be its guiding principle. It also holds that parents deserve control over their experience of birth and parenting, and that they need opportunities for mutual support and debriefing to enrich their experiences of birth and parenting – hence its emphasis on antenatal classes, and its support network for new parents.

The organisation is a crucial information-point for parents in need of up-to-date research to help make choices which are right for them on the issues they believe are important. Providing a consumer voice is another important area of the Trust's work, as it has always believed this is essential for the planning of better maternity services.

women who have had caesareans who feel like this: mothers who have had instrumental deliveries, or any other kind of delivery in which they felt powerless and unable to affect events, often suffer emotionally later. In the past there has been a tendency to talk fairly dismissively of 'afterbirth blues' and postnatal depression. Today, though, more is known about the psychological fallout of giving birth, and midwives, doctors and other professionals tend to be much more hesitant before using some catch-all phrase to cover what is, in fact, a complex mix of feelings.

This more empathetic approach is likely to become more wide-spread, and women who need to will hopefully be encouraged to talk through their birth experiences with counsellors to help them to work through their difficulties. So, whichever way our babies are born, and wherever we give birth there may be a future where every-one involved believes that treating a pregnant women well means more than sending her home with a baby: it means treating her holistically, recognising her as an individual who has dignity, rights and feelings and a point of view. If this lesson is being learned by the medical profession in the 1990s, the future for all childbearing women in Britain will be better than the past.

Bibliography

Books

Janet Balaskas 1981: *Active Birth*. Unwin, London.

Janet Balaskas 1979: *New Life*. Sidgwick & Jackson.

Janet Balaskas and Yehudi Gordon 1990: *Water Birth*. Unwin Paperbacks.

Josephine Barnes: *The Care of the Expectant Mother*. Pitman Medical
    Publishing Co Ltd.

1967: *Expecting a Baby*. BBC Publications.

Beverley Lawrence Beech 1987: *Who's Having Your Baby?* Camden Press,
    reprinted 1991 Bedford Square Press.

Gordon Bourne 1972: *Pregnancy*. Cassell.

Donald Buckley 1951: *The Way to Easy Childbirth*. Churchill and Co.

Dr Grantly Dick-Read 1942: *Childbirth Without Fear*. Heinemann.

Eve Stanton Featheringill 1951: *Primer for Pregnancy*. Simon & Schuster,
    New York.

Peter & Elizabeth Fenwick 1978: *The Baby Book for Fathers*. Angus and
    Robertson.

Dr John Gibbens 1962: *The Care of Young Babies*. Angus and Robertson.

Babara Glover, Christine Hodson 1985: *You and Your Premature Baby*.
    Sheldon Press.

Dr Alexander Gunn 1980: *Questions and Answers on Labour and Birth*.
    Argus, Watford.

Sally Inch 1982: *Birthrights: A Parents' Guide to Modern Childbirth*.
    Hutchinson.

Sheila Kitzinger 1962: *The Experience of Childbirth*. Penguin.

Sheila Kitzinger 1979: *The Good Birth Guide*. Fontana, reprinted 1983:
    New Good Birth Guide. Penguin.

Sheila Kitzinger 1986: *Pregnancy and Childbirth*. Penguin.

Sheila Kitzinger 1987: *Freedom and Choice in Childbirth*. Viking.

Sheila Kitzinger 1989: *The New Pregnancy and Childbirth*. Penguin.
Sheila Kitzinger 1994: *The Year After Childbirth*. Oxford University Press.
Nancy Kohner 1988: *Having a Baby*. BBC Books.
Dr Winifred de Kok 1957: *Your Baby and You*. Pan.
Frederick Leboyer 1977: *Birth Without Violence*. Fontana/Collins.
Mabel Liddiard 1923: *The Mothercraft Manual.* J and A Churchill.
    Eleventh ed. 1948.
Michel Odent 1986: *Birth Reborn*. Souvenir Press Ltd.
Michel Odent 1993: *The Nature of Birth and Breastfeeding*. Bergin and
    Garvey.
Elliot Philipp 1978: *Childbirth: A complete guide to every problem*.
    Fontana/Collins.
Angela Phillips and Jill Rakusen (eds) 1978: *Our Bodies Ourselves*. Penguin.
Dr Miriam Stoppard 1985: *Pregnancy and Birth Book*. Dorling Kindersley.
Nickey Wesson 1989: *Alternative Maternity*. Macdonald Optima, reprinted
    in 1995 Optima.
Mrs A A Woodman 1950: *The Sunday Express Baby Book*. Express
    Newspapers.
Erna Wright 1964: *The New Childbirth*. Universal Tandem. Reprinted in
    1965, 1966, 1967, 1968.

Periodicals

*Parents, Mother and Baby, New Generation, Pregnancy Plus, Your Complete
    Guide to Pregnancy and Birth, SHE Guide to Having a Baby.*

Other titles from NCT Publishing Ltd.

Becoming a Family

What will being a parent really be like? How will I cope with the basics like nappy changing?
What's the best way to ensure a good night's sleep? How will we manage the change in our lives?
Will sex ever be the same again?

Parenting is a hands-on skill – you learn as you go along but you can pick up most from the real 'experts': other parents. While there is often no 'right' or 'wrong' way to handle things, the suggestions and the experiences of other mothers and fathers can help you to decide what is right for you and your child. In *BECOMING A FAMILY*, the skills and expertise of other parents are combined with the essential facts and information that will enable you to adjust to being a parent.

Breastfeeding Your Baby

How does breastfeeding work? How do mothers breastfeed premature babies?
What's special about breast milk? Can you breastfeed twins? Will I enjoy breastfeeding?

More and more evidence is confirming that 'breast is best' for both baby and mother and increasing numbers of women are choosing to breastfeed, yet sometimes 'the natural thing to do' can be fraught with difficulties.

This book, written by three breastfeeding counsellors, draws on the experience of the National Childbirth Trust – which deals with over 114,000 enquiries a year – to answer the questions parents have about breastfeeding. In addition women share their experiences of breastfeeding, from the first few days when they are learning with their baby, through to becoming confident together, returning to work, and weaning.

Being Pregnant, Giving Birth

What are my choices for the birth? What do we need to know about antenatal tests?
What does labour really feel like? How can we best prepare ourselves for our baby?

BEING PREGNANT, GIVING BIRTH is a book for parents of the nineties: informative, enlightening and empowering. The combination of facts and parents sharing their experiences of the subject will help you to make informed choices, and to work in partnership with the health professionals to achieve the best outcome for you and your baby.

Work and Home
FINDING THE BALANCE

Can I cope with the demands of work and home? How do I deal with changed priorities?
Should we use a childminder, nanny or nursery? Can I work and breastfeed?
How do we avoid employing the 'nanny from hell'?

Mixing parenting with other work can be stressful and demanding but it also has its rewards and pleasures. In *WORK AND HOME* parents talk about how they have tried to achieve the right balance between work and home throughout the changing stages of family life. Mothers in all types of work situations – women who work full time, part time, freelance, job share or role reverse – describe how they juggle their working lives with caring for their families.

"Parents share their experiences about what having a baby is really like – a real plus."
PENELOPE LEACH, CHILDCARE EXPERT